MULTIPLI

Find each product.

If the product is ①, ㉑ or ㉛, color the space purple.

If the product is ②, ⑫, ㉜, ㊷ or ㋒, color the space green.

If the product is ③ or ㊳, color the space blue.

If the product is ④, ㉔ or ㊽, color the space red.

If the product is ⑤, ⑮, ㉕, ㉟ or ㊺, color the space brown.

If the product is ⑯ or ㊱, color the space yellow.

If the product is ⑦ or ㉗, color the space orange.

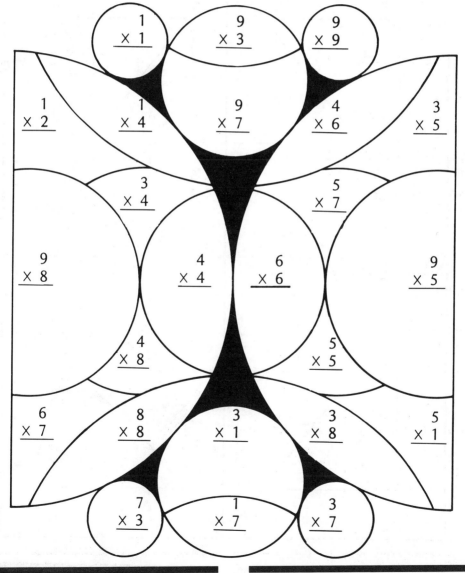

MULTIPLICATION

Find each product.
If the product is ⑥, ⑯, ㊱, or ㊶, color the space blue.
If the product is ⑧, ㉘, or ㊽, color the space yellow.
If the product is ⑨, ⑩, ⑳, ㉚, ㊵, or ㊾, color the space orange.

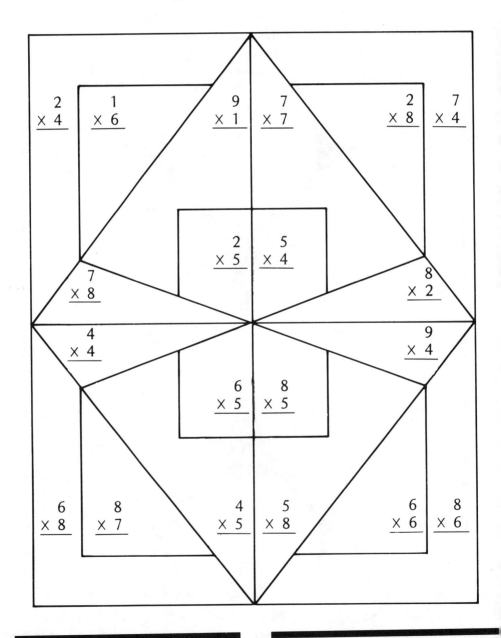

MULTIPLICATION

Find each product.

If the product is (160), color the space green.

If the product is (210), color the space orange.

If the product is (288), color the space purple.

If the product is (378), color the space red.

If the product is (504), color the space brown.

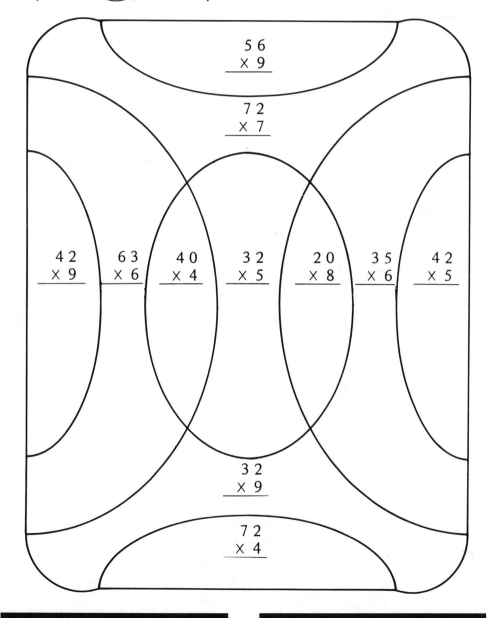

MULTIPLICATION

Find each product.

If the product is ⑤⓪, ⑭⓪, ①⑤③, ①⑦⓪, ④⓪⓪, ④①⓪, ④⑤⑥, or ⑤③①,
color the space green.

If the product is ⑨⑨, ①②⓪, ①②⑥, ①④⑦, ③⑤⓪, ③⑦⑧, ⑤⑦⑥, or ⑥④⓪,
color the space blue.

If the product is ①⑥⓪, ①⑥⑧, ②④⓪, ②⑤②, ③⑥⓪, ③⑧⓪, ⑤⑥⑦, or ⑦⓪②,
color the space yellow.

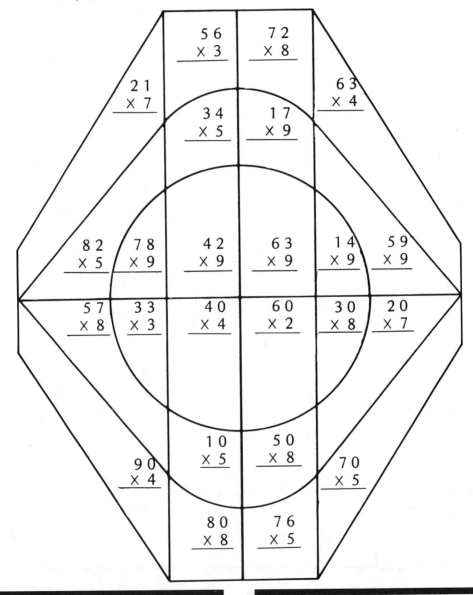

MULTIPLICATION

Find each product.
If the product is (955), (1,969), (3,904) or (8,361), color the space yellow.
If the product is (1,302), (1,768), (2,769), (3,730) or (4,175), color the space green.
If the product is (1,371), (1,694), (1,955) or (2,889), color the space red.

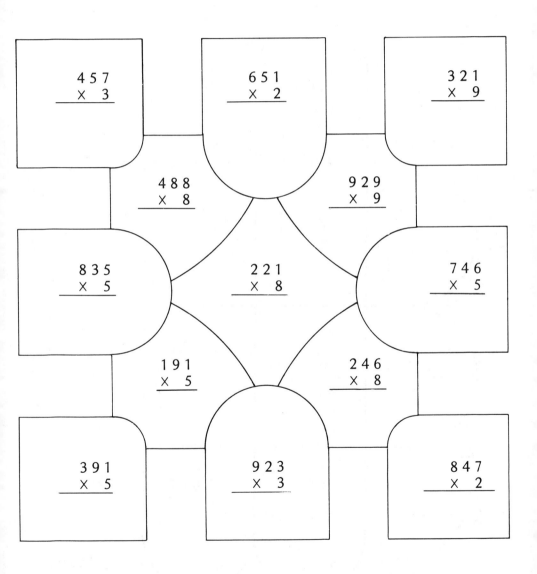

MULTIPLICATION

Find each product.

If the product is (5,476), or (9,742), color the space blue.

If the product is (6,190), (18,213), (34,800), or (45,126), color the space red.

If the product is (12,806), (14,604), (45,792), or (49,476), color the space orange.

If the product is (29,970) or (36,684), color the space purple.

3,651 × 4	1,238 × 5

7,521 × 6	1,369 × 4	4,076 × 9	5,724 × 8

6,403 × 2	3,330 × 9	4,871 × 2	6,071 × 3

4,350 × 8	7,068 × 7

MULTIPLICATION

Find each product.
If the product is 546, 1,134, 1,449, 1,568, or 5,929, color the space yellow.
If the product is 960, 1,280, or 1,332, color the space blue.
If the product is 1,375, 1,748, or 6,480, color the space purple.

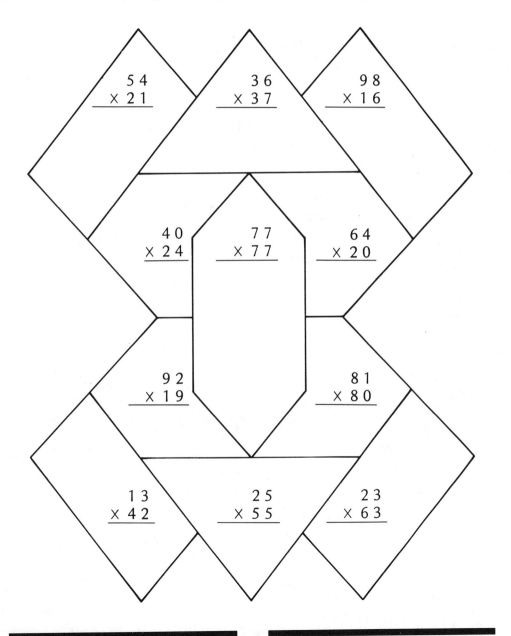

$$
\begin{array}{r} 5\,4 \\ \times\ 2\,1 \\ \hline \end{array}
\qquad
\begin{array}{r} 3\,6 \\ \times\ 3\,7 \\ \hline \end{array}
\qquad
\begin{array}{r} 9\,8 \\ \times\ 1\,6 \\ \hline \end{array}
$$

$$
\begin{array}{r} 4\,0 \\ \times\ 2\,4 \\ \hline \end{array}
\qquad
\begin{array}{r} 7\,7 \\ \times\ 7\,7 \\ \hline \end{array}
\qquad
\begin{array}{r} 6\,4 \\ \times\ 2\,0 \\ \hline \end{array}
$$

$$
\begin{array}{r} 9\,2 \\ \times\ 1\,9 \\ \hline \end{array}
\qquad\qquad
\begin{array}{r} 8\,1 \\ \times\ 8\,0 \\ \hline \end{array}
$$

$$
\begin{array}{r} 1\,3 \\ \times\ 4\,2 \\ \hline \end{array}
\qquad
\begin{array}{r} 2\,5 \\ \times\ 5\,5 \\ \hline \end{array}
\qquad
\begin{array}{r} 2\,3 \\ \times\ 6\,3 \\ \hline \end{array}
$$

MULTIPLICATION

Find each product.

If the product is (67,446), (73,380), (79,506), or (157,919), color the space red.

If the product is (35,160), (154,014), (225,325), or (289,728),
color the space purple.

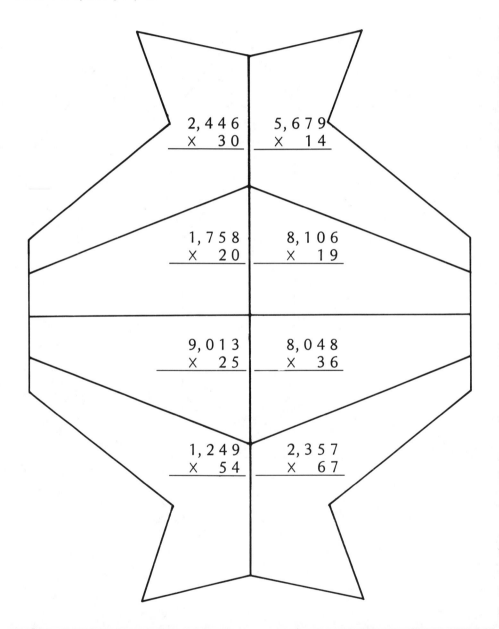

$$2,446 \times 30$$

$$5,679 \times 14$$

$$1,758 \times 20$$

$$8,106 \times 19$$

$$9,013 \times 25$$

$$8,048 \times 36$$

$$1,249 \times 54$$

$$2,357 \times 67$$

MULTIPLICATION

Find each product.
If the product is 43,014, 71,360, 95,760 or 568,420, color the space brown.
If the product is 53,505, 251,515 or 265,350, color the space red.
If the product is 55,242, 579,126 or 233,016, color the space green.

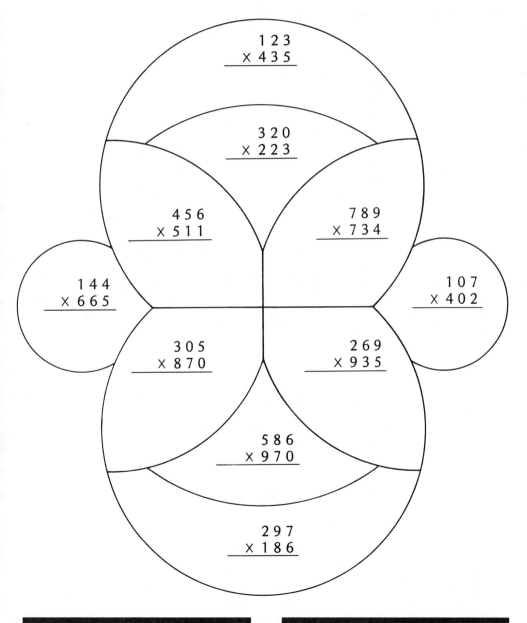

DIVISION

Find each quotient.
If the quotient is ②, color the space red.
If the quotient is ④, color the space green.
If the quotient is ⑤ or ⑧, color the space yellow.
If the quotient is ⑥, color the space orange.
If the quotient is ⑦, color the space purple.
If the quotient is ⑨, color the space blue.

		2⟌1 0				
	9⟌4 5	4⟌1 6	4⟌3 6			
	4⟌2 0	9⟌3 6	2⟌1 8	2⟌1 4	8⟌1 6	
7⟌3 5	7⟌2 8	3⟌2 7	5⟌3 5	6⟌1 2	6⟌3 6	3⟌2 4
	5⟌4 5	4⟌2 8	2⟌4	4⟌2 4	9⟌7 2	
		3⟌6	8⟌4 8	4⟌3 2		
			6⟌4 8			

DIVISION

Find each quotient.
If the quotient is ①, color the space brown.
If the quotient is ③, color the space orange.
If the quotient is ⑧, color the space yellow.
If the quotient is ⑨, color the space red.

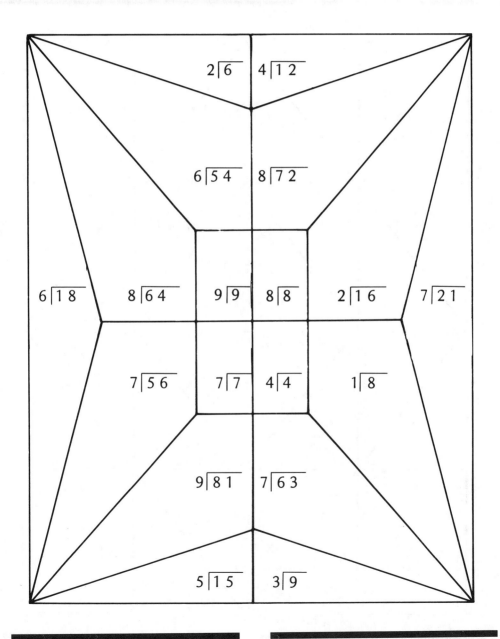

Math in Color IF0191   ©1992 Instructional Fair, Inc.

DIVISION

Find each quotient.
If the quotient is (16), (23), (34), or (42), color the space purple.
If the quotient is (11), (12), or (28), color the space green.
If the quotient is (13), (14), or (33), color the space yellow.

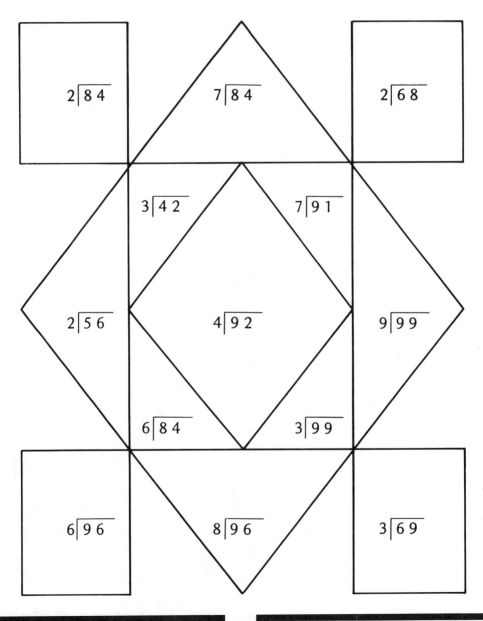

DIVISION

Find each quotient.
If the quotient is ②, color the space purple.
If the quotient is ③, color the space green.
If the quotient is ④, color the space blue.
If the quotient is ⑥, color the space yellow.

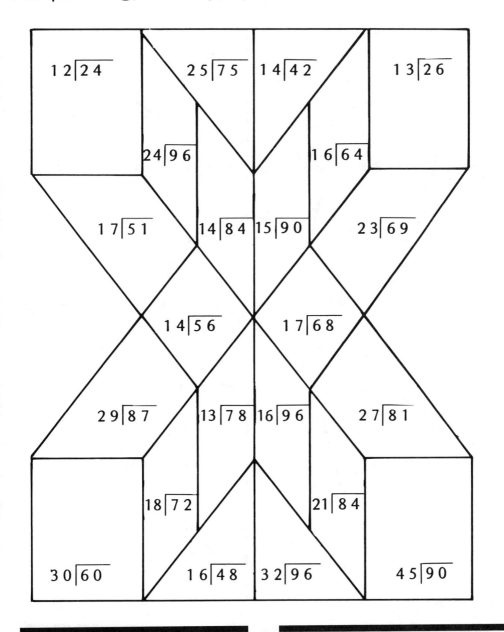

Math in Color IF0191   ©1992 Instructional Fair, Inc.

DIVISION

Find each quotient.
If the quotient is ③, color the space purple.
If the quotient is ④, color the space yellow.
If the quotient is ⑤, color the space green.

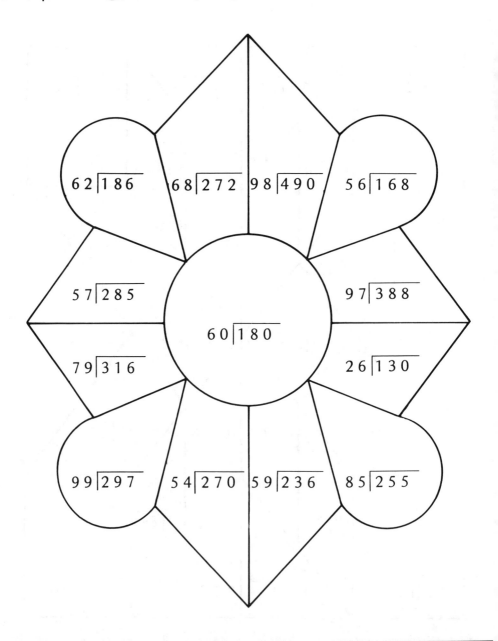

DIVISION

Find each quotient.
If the quotient is ⑥ color the space blue.
If the quotient is ⑦, color the space red.
If the quotient is ⑧, color the space green.
If the quotient is ⑨, color the space orange.

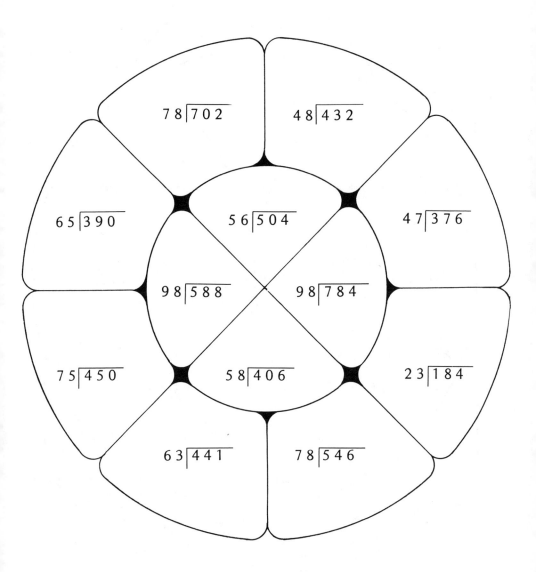

DIVISION

Find each quotient.
If the quotient is ⑭, color the space green.
If the quotient is ⑮, color the space red.
If the quotient is ⑯, color the space blue.
If the quotient is ⑰, color the space yellow.

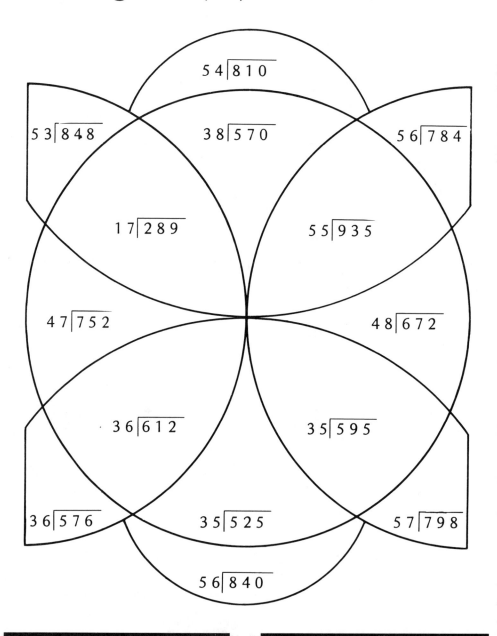

DIVISION

Find each quotient.
If the quotient is ㊴, color the space blue.
If the quotient is ㊷, color the space red.
If the quotient is ㊼, color the space green.

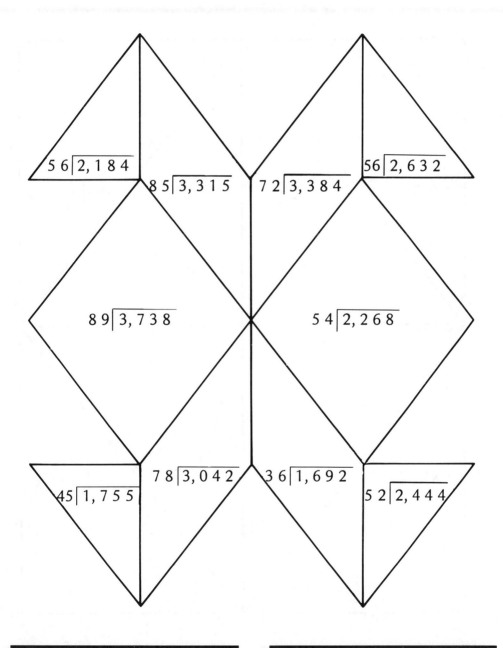

DIVISION

Find each quotient.
If the quotient is ⑰, color the space purple.
If the quotient is ⑲, color the space green.

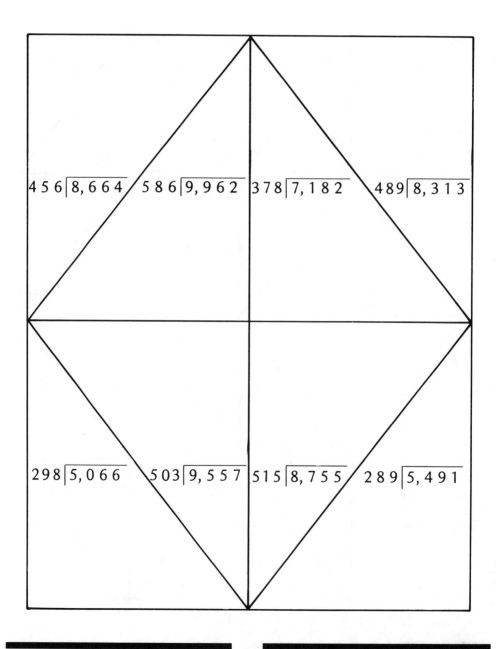

$4\,5\,6\,\overline{\smash{)}\,8,6\,6\,4}$ $5\,8\,6\,\overline{\smash{)}\,9,9\,6\,2}$ $3\,7\,8\,\overline{\smash{)}\,7,1\,8\,2}$ $4\,8\,9\,\overline{\smash{)}\,8,3\,1\,3}$

$2\,9\,8\,\overline{\smash{)}\,5,0\,6\,6}$ $5\,0\,3\,\overline{\smash{)}\,9,5\,5\,7}$ $5\,1\,5\,\overline{\smash{)}\,8,7\,5\,5}$ $2\,8\,9\,\overline{\smash{)}\,5,4\,9\,1}$

DECIMALS

Find each sum.
If the sum is (1.2), color the space blue.
If the sum is (1.3), color the space yellow.
If the sum is (1.4), color the space red.

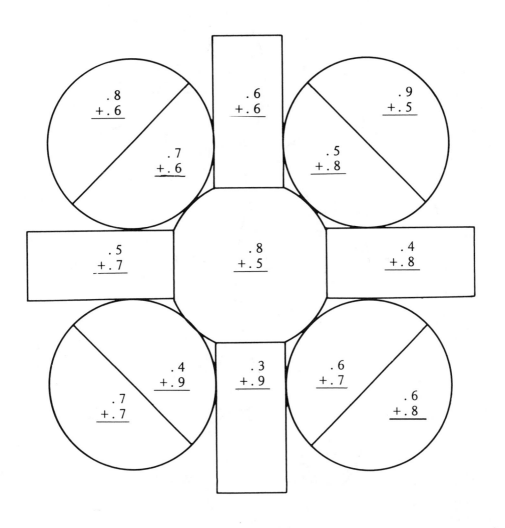

DECIMALS

Find each sum.

If the sum is (.6), color the space brown.

If the sum is (.7), color the space green.

If the sum is (3.2), color the space orange.

If the sum is (3.3), color the space purple.

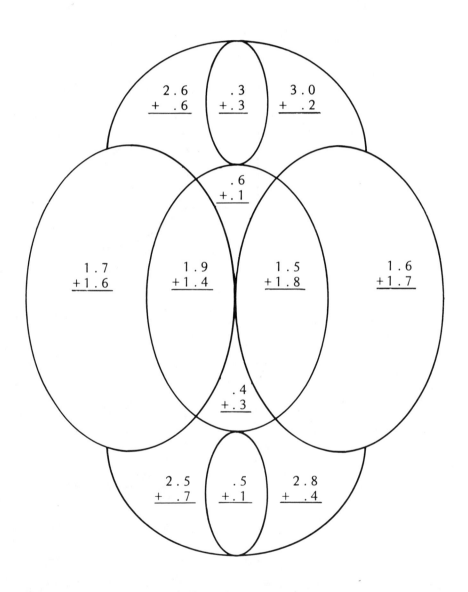

DECIMALS

Find each sum.
If the sum is (1.23), color the space orange.
If the sum is (1.24), color the space red.
If the sum is (1.25), color the space yellow.
If the sum is (1.35), color the space blue.

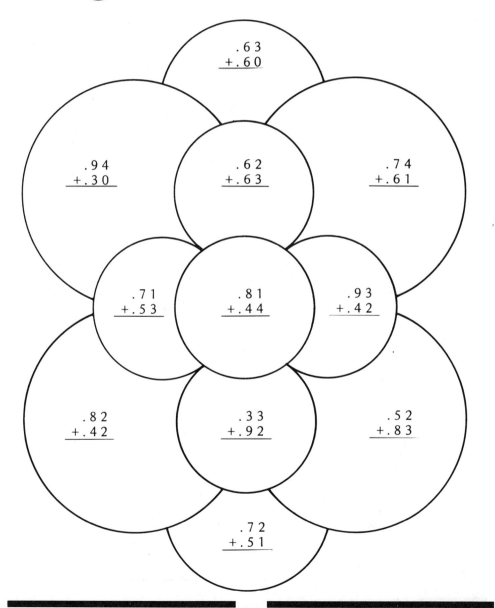

DECIMALS

Find each sum.
If the sum is (1.243), (1.86), (2.28), (8.52) or (10.6), color the space blue.
If the sum is (.97), (11.48), (2.29), (2.42) or (7.97), color the space yellow.
If the sum is (1.16), (1.85) or (11.6), color the space green.

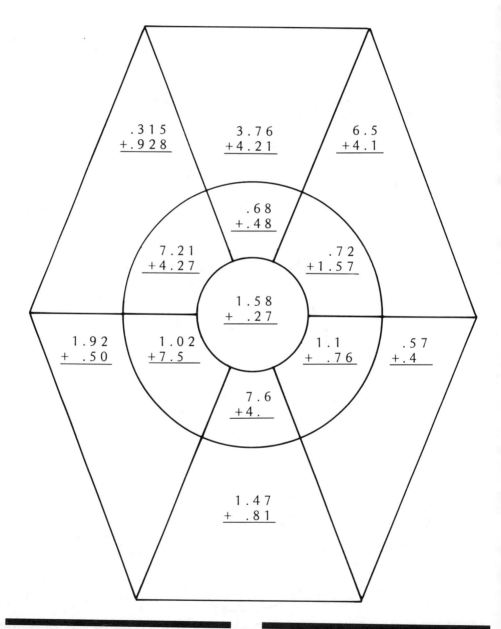

DECIMALS

Find each difference.
If the difference is ③, color the space yellow.
If the difference is ④, color the space red.
If the difference is ⑤, color the space orange.
If the difference is ⑥, color the space green.

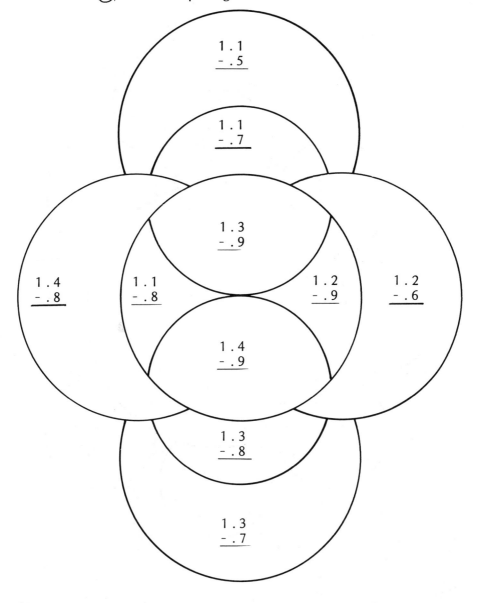

DECIMALS

Find each difference.
If the difference is (1.7), color the space yellow.
If the difference is (1.8), color the space green.
If the difference is (1.9), color the space purple.

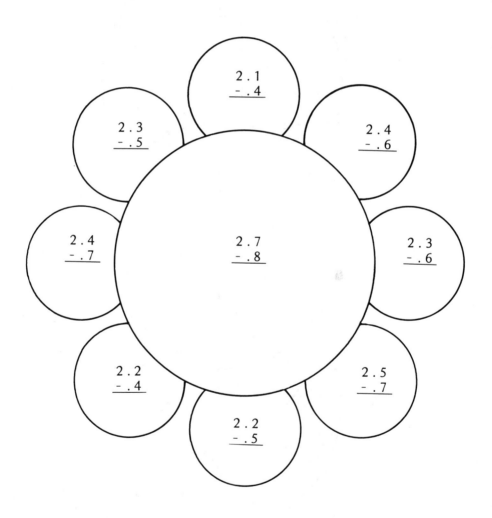

DECIMALS

Find each difference.
If the difference is ⑨, ⑴⑴⑴, ⑴⑵⑵, ②⑥④ or ⑺⑴⑨, color the space yellow.
If the difference is ⑥⑥, ⑴⑩⑩ or ⑧⑴, color the space green.
If the difference is ②, ⑺⑥, ⑧④, ⑨⑤ or ⑷⑨, color the space blue.
If the difference is ⑴⑤, ⑴⑨, ③⑨ or ④⑨⑴, color the space brown.

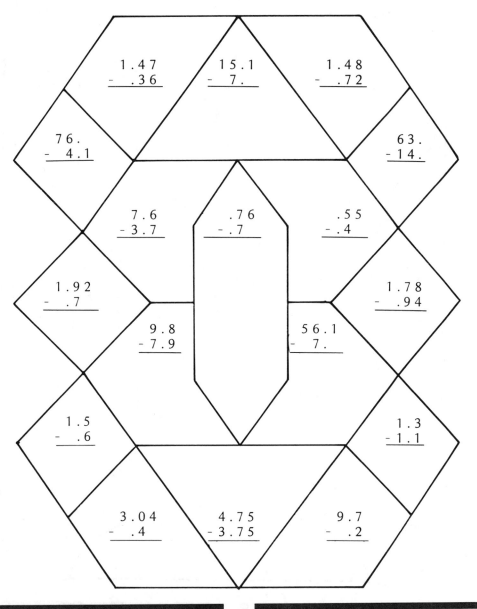

DECIMALS

Find each difference.
If the difference is (1.83), color the space yellow.
If the difference is (2.73), color the space blue.
If the difference is (4.83), color the space green.

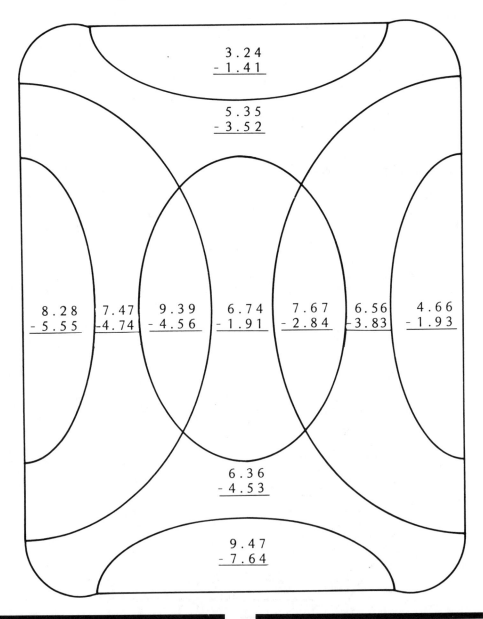

$$
\begin{array}{r}
3.24 \\
-1.41 \\
\end{array}
$$

$$
\begin{array}{r}
5.35 \\
-3.52 \\
\end{array}
$$

$$
\begin{array}{r}
8.28 \\
-5.55 \\
\end{array}
\quad
\begin{array}{r}
7.47 \\
-4.74 \\
\end{array}
\quad
\begin{array}{r}
9.39 \\
-4.56 \\
\end{array}
\quad
\begin{array}{r}
6.74 \\
-1.91 \\
\end{array}
\quad
\begin{array}{r}
7.67 \\
-2.84 \\
\end{array}
\quad
\begin{array}{r}
6.56 \\
-3.83 \\
\end{array}
\quad
\begin{array}{r}
4.66 \\
-1.93 \\
\end{array}
$$

$$
\begin{array}{r}
6.36 \\
-4.53 \\
\end{array}
$$

$$
\begin{array}{r}
9.47 \\
-7.64 \\
\end{array}
$$

DECIMALS

Find each sum or difference.
If the answer is (.5), color the space yellow.
If the answer is (.6), color the space blue.
If the answer is (.7), color the space orange.
If the answer is (.8), color the space green.

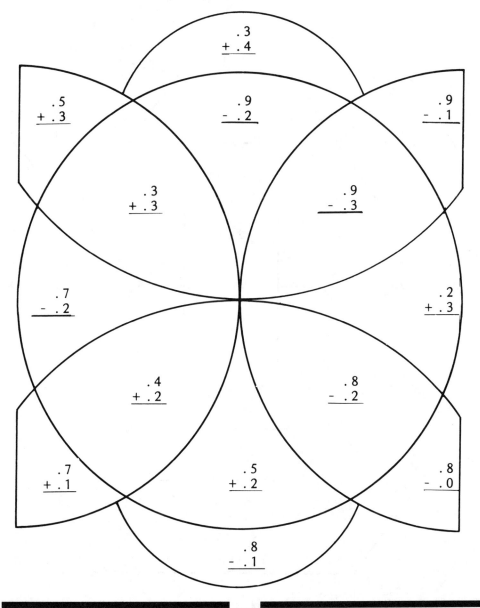

DECIMALS

Find each sum or difference.
If the answer is ④⑥, color the space yellow.
If the answer is ⑦⑧, color the space green.
If the answer is ⑧⑦, color the space purple.

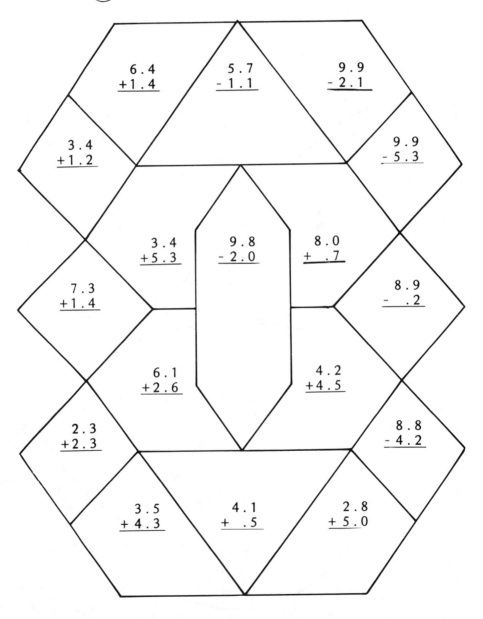

DECIMALS

Find each sum or difference.
If the answer is ⑤③, color the space purple.
If the answer is ⑥④, color the space green.
If the answer is ⑤③, color the space red.
If the answer is ⑥④, color the space yellow.

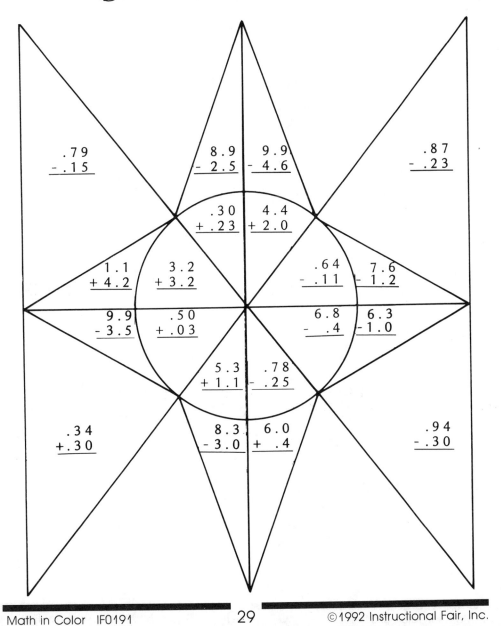

DECIMALS

Find each sum or difference.

If the answer is ⟨.313⟩, color the space purple.

If the answer is ⟨3.13⟩, color the space orange.

If the answer is ⟨5.53⟩, color the space yellow.

If the answer is ⟨55.3⟩, color the space blue.

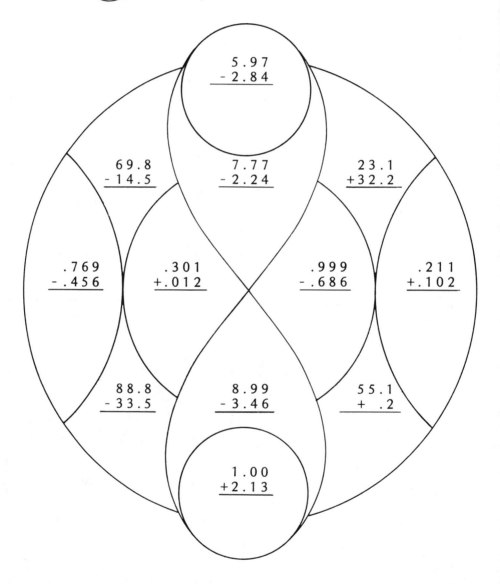

DECIMALS

Find each sum or difference.
If the answer is ⊗, ⑦, ⑩, ⑩⑤ or ⑪⑪, color the space purple.
If the answer is ⑦⑧, ②⑪, ⑤⑨ or ⑫⑪, color the space red.
If the answer is ⑮, ③③④, ③⑦⑪, ④⑨, ⑨⑪ or ⑰⑤, color the space yellow.

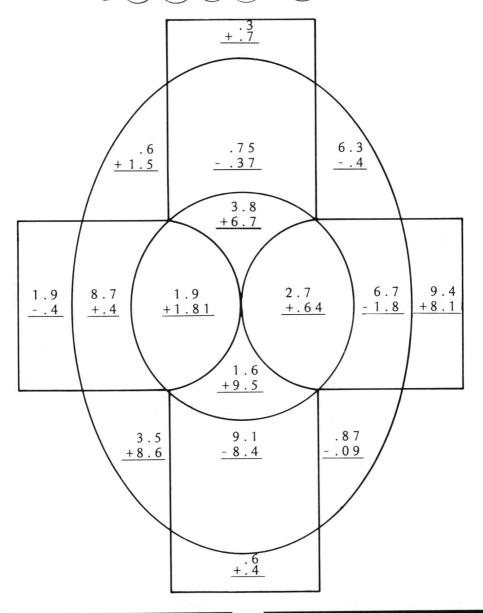

$$\begin{array}{r} .3 \\ +\ .7 \\ \hline \end{array}$$

$$\begin{array}{r} .6 \\ +1.5 \\ \hline \end{array}$$
$$\begin{array}{r} .75 \\ -\ .37 \\ \hline \end{array}$$
$$\begin{array}{r} 6.3 \\ -\ .4 \\ \hline \end{array}$$

$$\begin{array}{r} 3.8 \\ +6.7 \\ \hline \end{array}$$

$$\begin{array}{r} 1.9 \\ -\ .4 \\ \hline \end{array}$$
$$\begin{array}{r} 8.7 \\ +\ .4 \\ \hline \end{array}$$
$$\begin{array}{r} 1.9 \\ +1.81 \\ \hline \end{array}$$
$$\begin{array}{r} 2.7 \\ +\ .64 \\ \hline \end{array}$$
$$\begin{array}{r} 6.7 \\ -1.8 \\ \hline \end{array}$$
$$\begin{array}{r} 9.4 \\ +8.1 \\ \hline \end{array}$$

$$\begin{array}{r} 1.6 \\ +9.5 \\ \hline \end{array}$$

$$\begin{array}{r} 3.5 \\ +8.6 \\ \hline \end{array}$$
$$\begin{array}{r} 9.1 \\ -8.4 \\ \hline \end{array}$$
$$\begin{array}{r} .87 \\ -\ .09 \\ \hline \end{array}$$

$$\begin{array}{r} .6 \\ +\ .4 \\ \hline \end{array}$$

DECIMALS

Find each sum or difference.
If the answer is $.16$, $.31$, $.68$, $.78$, $.814$ or 3.2, color the space purple.
If the answer is $.17$, $.32$, 1.27, 8.9 or 11.5, color the space yellow.
If the answer is $.37$, 1.12 or 1.44, color the space orange.

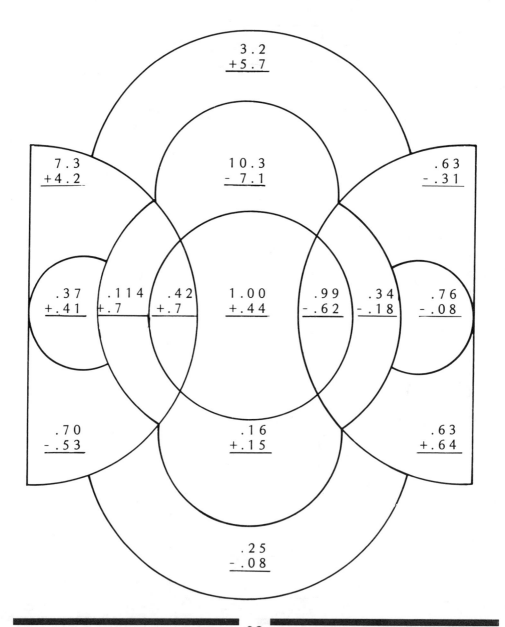

DECIMALS

Find each sum or difference.

If the answer is (.14), (2.0), (65.1) or (110.1), color the space brown.

If the answer is (.20), (1.14), (6.0) or (7.7), color the space orange.

If the answer is (.9), (4.9), (6.7), (7.0), (12.3) or (60.7), color the space red.

If the answer is (1.84), (6.4), (7.5) or (62.5), color the space green.

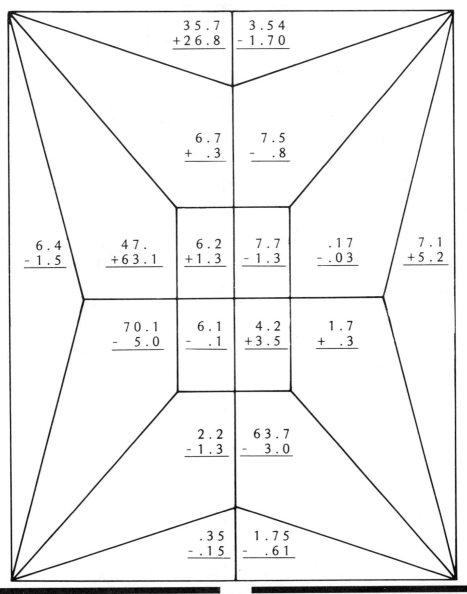

DECIMALS

Find each sum or difference.

If the answer is ㉑, ㉚, ㉘⓪, ①.⓪②, ①.⑧⑨, ③.②, ⑥.⑨ or ①①.⑤,
   color the space green.

If the answer is ㉝, ㉒, ①.①⓪, ①.⑦, ⑥.④, ⑦.③ or ⑦.⑨, color the space red.

If the answer is ㉞, ㉒, ㊽, ㊏⑥, ㊑①, ①.①⑦, ①.②⑥ or ①.⑨③,
   color the space orange.

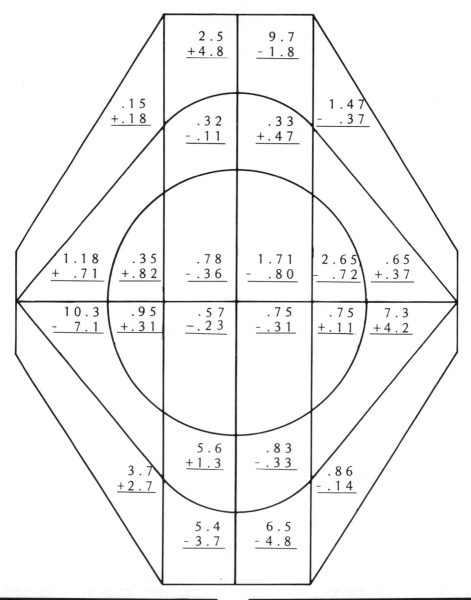

DECIMALS

Find each product.
If the product is ③.②, ⑨.⑧, ⑱.④ or ㉒.②, color the space purple.
If the product is ③.⑥, ⑭.⑧, ⑯.② or ㉒.⑧, color the space green.
If the product is ④.⑤, color the space red.
If the product is ⑨.⓪, color the space yellow.

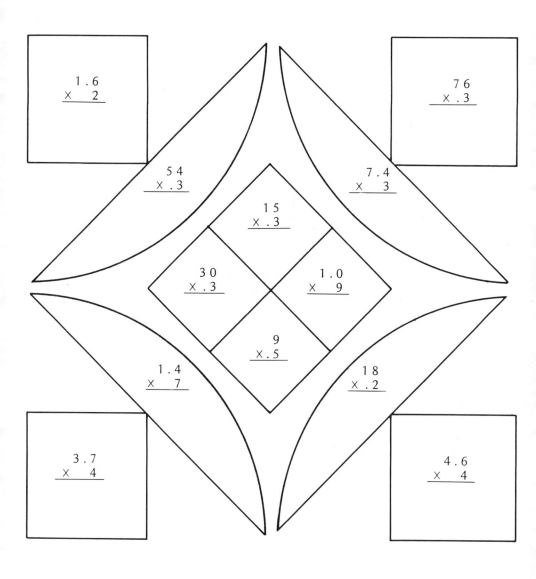

DECIMALS

Find each product.
If the product is (14.4), (74.4), (169.4) or (194.4), color the space blue.
If the product is (31.5), (35.2), (57.8), (147.0) or (189.0), color the space purple.
If the product is (31.9), (53.3), (80.5) or (149.6), color the space yellow.

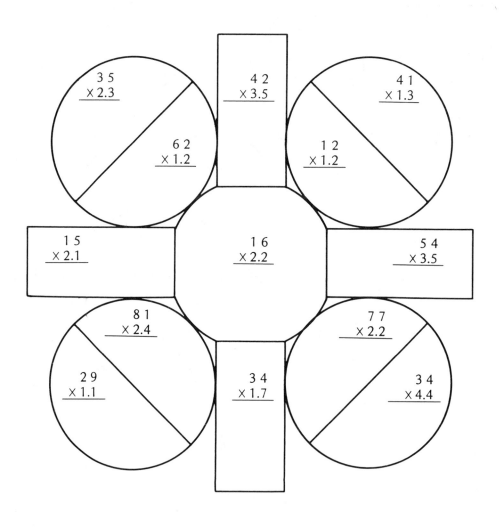

Tutor's Guide

This Tutor's Guide contains answer keys for Math in Color - Grades 5-6. Pull it out from the book to use as a guide.

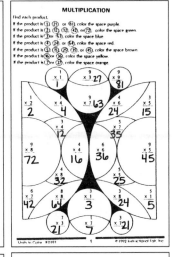

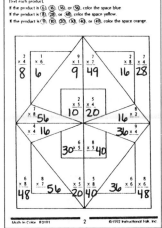

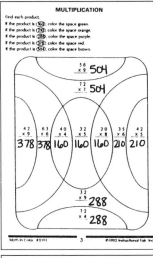

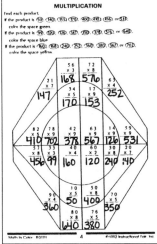

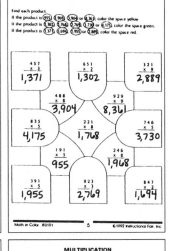

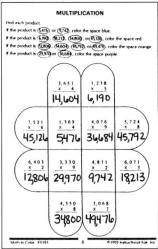

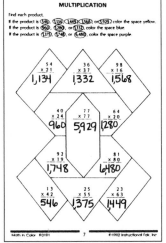

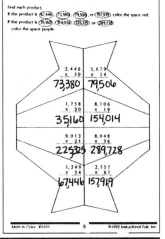

MULTIPLICATION

Find each product.
If the product is 43,014, 71,360, 95,760, or 568,420, color the space brown.
If the product is 53,505, 251,515, or 265,360, color the space red.
If the product is 55,242, 579,126, or 233,016, color the space green.

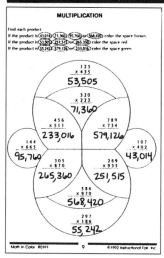

DIVISION

Find each quotient.
If the quotient is 2, color the space red.
If the quotient is 4, color the space green.
If the quotient is 5 or 8, color the space yellow.
If the quotient is 6, color the space orange.
If the quotient is 7, color the space purple.
If the quotient is 9, color the space blue.

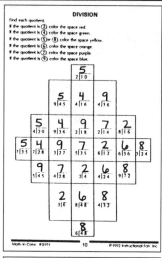

DIVISION

Find each quotient.
If the quotient is 1, color the space brown.
If the quotient is 3, color the space orange.
If the quotient is 8, color the space yellow.
If the quotient is 9, color the space red.

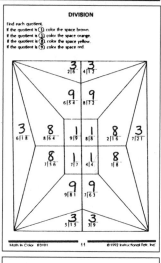

DIVISION

Find each quotient.
If the quotient is 16, 23, 34, or 42, color the space purple.
If the quotient is 11, 12, or 28, color the space green.
If the quotient is 13, 14, or 33, color the space yellow.

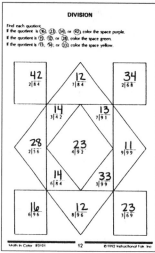

DIVISION

Find each quotient.
If the quotient is 2, color the space purple.
If the quotient is 3, color the space red.
If the quotient is 4, color the space blue.
If the quotient is 6, color the space yellow.

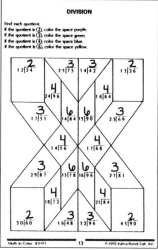

DIVISION

Find each quotient.
If the quotient is 3, color the space purple.
If the quotient is 4, color the space yellow.
If the quotient is 5, color the space green.

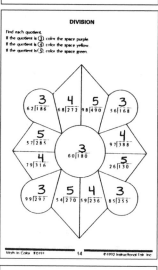

DIVISION

Find each quotient.
If the quotient is 6, color the space blue.
If the quotient is 7, color the space red.
If the quotient is 8, color the space green.
If the quotient is 9, color the space orange.

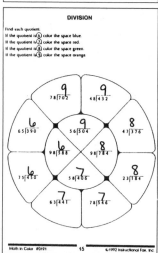

DIVISION

Find each quotient.
If the quotient is 14, color the space green.
If the quotient is 15, color the space red.
If the quotient is 16, color the space blue.
If the quotient is 17, color the space yellow.

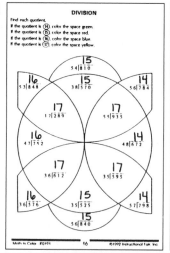

DIVISION

Find each quotient.
If the quotient is 39, color the space blue.
If the quotient is 42, color the space red.
If the quotient is 47, color the space green.

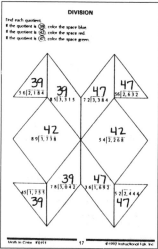

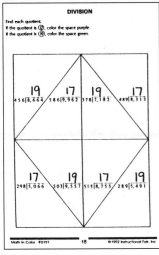
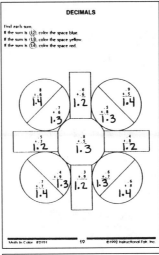
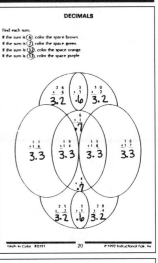
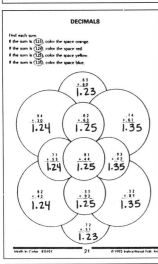
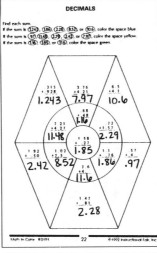
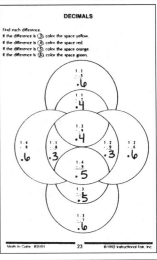
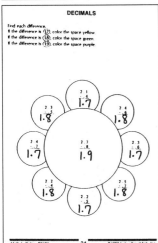
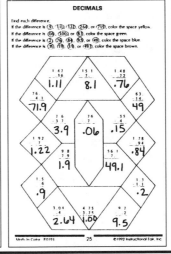
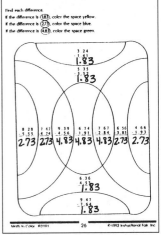

DECIMALS

Find each sum or difference.
If the answer is .5, color the space yellow.
If the answer is .6, color the space blue.
If the answer is .7, color the space orange.
If the answer is .8, color the space green.

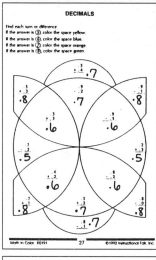

Math in Color #0191   27   ©1992 Instructional Fair, Inc.

DECIMALS

Find each sum or difference.
If the answer is 4.6, color the space yellow.
If the answer is 7.8, color the space green.
If the answer is 8.7, color the space purple.

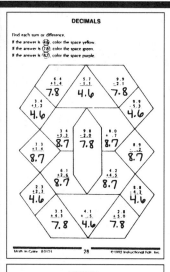

Math in Color #0191   28   ©1992 Instructional Fair, Inc.

DECIMALS

Find each sum or difference.
If the answer is .53, color the space purple.
If the answer is .64, color the space green.
If the answer is 5.3, color the space red.
If the answer is 6.4, color the space yellow.

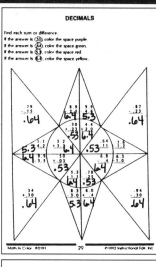

Math in Color #0191   29   ©1992 Instructional Fair, Inc.

DECIMALS

Find each sum or difference.
If the answer is 3.13, color the space purple.
If the answer is .313, color the space orange.
If the answer is 5.53, color the space yellow.
If the answer is 55.3, color the space blue.

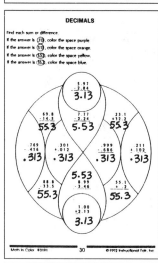

Math in Color #0191   30   ©1992 Instructional Fair, Inc.

DECIMALS

Find each sum or difference.
If the answer is .38, .7, 1.0, 10.5, or 11.1, color the space purple.
If the answer is .78, 2.1, 5.9, or 12.1, color the space red.
If the answer is 1.5, 3.34, 3.71, 4.9, 9.1, or 17.5, color the space yellow.

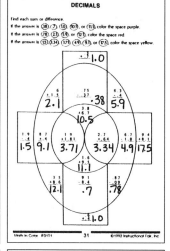

Math in Color #0191   31   ©1992 Instructional Fair, Inc.

DECIMALS

Find each sum or difference.
If the answer is .16, .31, .68, .78, .814, or .32, color the space purple.
If the answer is .17, .32, 1.27, 1.42, 8.9, or 11.5, color the space yellow.
If the answer is .37, 1.12, or 1.44, color the space orange.

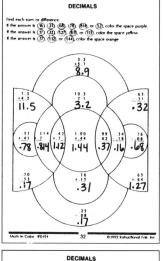

Math in Color #0191   32   ©1992 Instructional Fair, Inc.

DECIMALS

Find each sum or difference.
If the answer is 1.14, 12.0, 65.1, or 110.1, color the space brown.
If the answer is .20, .14, 6.0, or 7.7, color the space orange.
If the answer is .9, 4.9, 6.7, 12.3, or 60.7, color the space red.
If the answer is 1.84, 6.4, 7.5, or 62.5, color the space green.

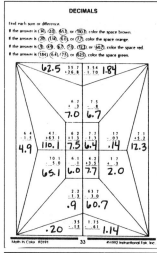

Math in Color #0191   33   ©1992 Instructional Fair, Inc.

DECIMALS

Find each sum or difference.
If the answer is .21, .50, .80, 1.02, 1.09, .32, .69, or 1.15, color the space green.
If the answer is .33, .72, 1.10, .17, 6.4, 7.3, or 7.9, color the space red.
If the answer is .34, .42, .44, .86, .91, 1.26, or 1.93, color the space orange.

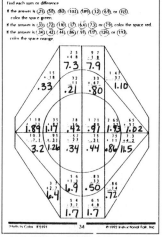

Math in Color #0191   34   ©1992 Instructional Fair, Inc.

DECIMALS

Find each product.
If the product is 3.2, 9.8, 18.4, or 22.2, color the space purple.
If the product is 3.6, 14.8, 16.2, or 22.8, color the space green.
If the product is 4.5, color the space red.
If the product is 9.0, color the space yellow.

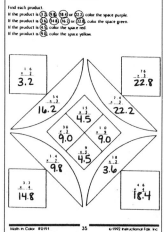

Math in Color #0191   35   ©1992 Instructional Fair, Inc.

Find each product.
If the product is 14.4, 74.4, 169.4, or 194.4, color the space blue.
If the product is 31.5, 35.2, 57.8, 147.0, or 189.0, color the space purple.
If the product is 31.9, 53.3, 80.5, or 149.6, color the space yellow.

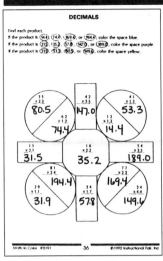

Find each product.
If the product is .36, 1.15, 2.56, or 3.44, color the space red.
If the product is 1.18, or 1.68, color the space brown.
If the product is 4.56, 6.30, 8.64, or 26.95, color the space yellow.
If the product is 5.46, 14.62, 15.12, or 19.04, color the space orange.

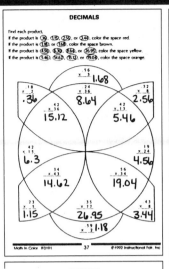

Find each product.
If the product is 1.28, 2.35, or 3.24, color the space red.
If the product is 5.1, 3.9, or 5.10, color the space blue.
If the product is 18.36, or 15.96, color the space green.
If the product is 24, or 30.24, color the space orange.
If the product is 1.12, 1.28, 1.35, 9.90, 18.36, or 22.32, color the space yellow.

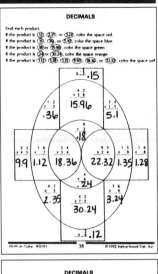

Find each product.
If the product is .045, .224, or .185, color the space orange.
If the product is .060, .105, 1.136, or 1.998, color the space red.
If the product is .094, 1.848, or 2.821, color the space yellow.

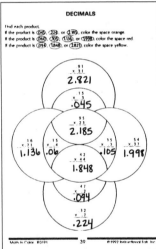

Find each product.
If the product is .0646, or .4521, color the space purple.
If the product is .1980, .2491, or .2520, color the space yellow.
If the product is .3105, or 1.2524, color the space red.
If the product is 1.1680, or 1.5300, color the space orange.

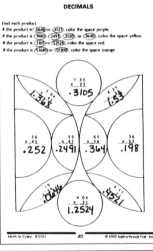

Find each product.
If the product is .15, .28, .36, or .91, color the space green.
If the product is .225, .370, 2.98, or 219.6, color the space purple.
If the product is 3.6, 2.646, 6.256, 30.0, or 277.5, color the space orange.

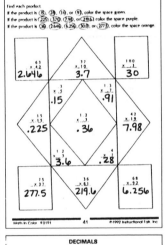

Find each quotient.
If the quotient is 1.2, color the space red.
If the quotient is 1.3, color the space yellow.
If the quotient is 1.7, color the space purple.

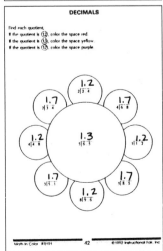

Find each quotient.
If the quotient is 8.5, color the space green.
If the quotient is 9.5, color the space red.
If the quotient is 16.5, color the space purple.
If the quotient is 22.5, color the space yellow.

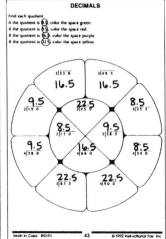

Find each quotient.
If the quotient is 18.3, color the space green.
If the quotient is 19.1, color the space yellow.
If the quotient is 19.5, color the space blue.

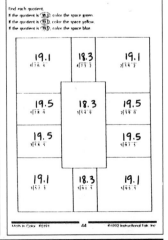

DECIMALS

Find each quotient.
If the quotient is (.48), color the space green.
If the quotient is (.54), color the space yellow.
If the quotient is (.48), color the space blue.

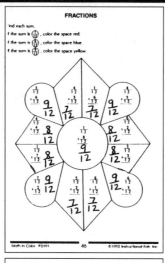

FRACTIONS

Find each sum.
If the sum is $\frac{7}{12}$, color the space red.
If the sum is $\frac{8}{12}$, color the space blue.
If the sum is $\frac{9}{12}$, color the space yellow.

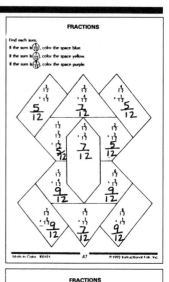

FRACTIONS

Find each sum.
If the sum is $\frac{7}{12}$, color the space blue.
If the sum is $\frac{9}{12}$, color the space yellow.
If the sum is $\frac{5}{12}$, color the space purple.

FRACTIONS

Find each difference.
If the difference is $\frac{1}{8}$, color the space yellow.
If the difference is $\frac{2}{8}$, color the space blue.
If the difference is $\frac{3}{8}$, color the space orange.
If the difference is $\frac{4}{8}$, color the space purple.

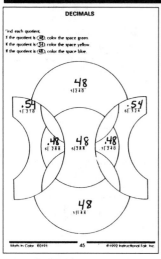

FRACTIONS

Find each difference.
If the difference is $\frac{7}{12}$, color the space yellow.
If the difference is $\frac{5}{12}$, color the space blue.
If the difference is $\frac{3}{12}$, color the space red.
If the difference is $\frac{9}{12}$, color the space orange.

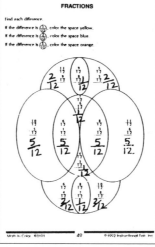

FRACTIONS

Find each sum or difference.
If the answer is $\frac{7}{12}$, color the space green.
If the answer is $\frac{9}{12}$, color the space blue.
If the answer is $\frac{8}{12}$, color the space red.
If the answer is $\frac{6}{12}$, color the space purple.

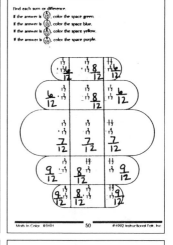

FRACTIONS

If the pair of fractions is equivalent, color the space green.
If the pair of fractions is not equivalent, color the space red.

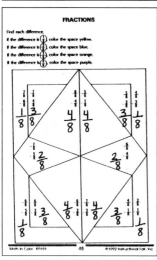

FRACTIONS

If the pair of fractions is equivalent, color the space yellow.
If the pair of fractions is not equivalent, color the space green.

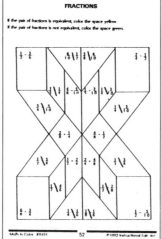

FRACTIONS

Write a numeral to complete each pair of equivalent fractions.
If the answer is (2), color the space blue.
If the answer is (3), color the space yellow.
If the answer is (4), color the space green.
If the answer is (8), color the space purple.

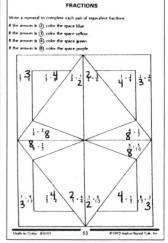

FRACTIONS

Write a numeral to complete each pair of equivalent fractions.
If the answer is (2), color the space green.
If the answer is (4), color the space blue.
If the answer is (5), color the space orange.
If the answer is (10), color the space purple.

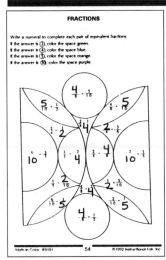

FRACTIONS

Reduce each fraction to lowest terms.
If the answer is (1/4), color the space red.
If the answer is (1/2), color the space yellow.
If the answer is (1/3), color the space blue.

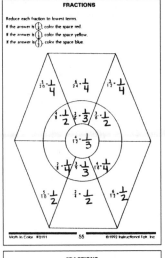

FRACTIONS

Reduce each fraction to lowest terms.
If the answer is (1/2), color the space blue.
If the answer is (1/4), color the space orange.
If the answer is (1/3), color the space green.

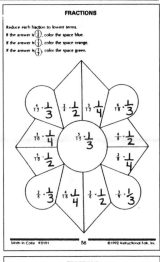

FRACTIONS

Reduce each fraction to lowest terms.
If the answer is (1/2), color the space purple.
If the answer is (1/5), color the space orange.
If the answer is (3/4), color the space yellow.
If the answer is (2/3), color the space red.

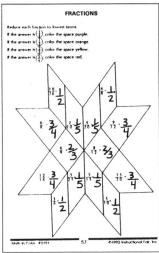

FRACTIONS

Write the least common denominator for each set of fractions.
If the least common denominator is (1/4), color the space yellow.
If the least common denominator is (1/6), color the space green.
If the least common denominator is (1/8), color the space purple.
If the least common denominator is (1/12), color the space red.

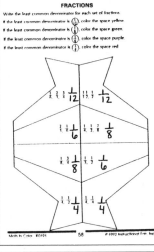

FRACTIONS

Write the least common denominator for each set of fractions.
If the least common denominator is (1/8), color the space red.
If the least common denominator is (1/12), color the space purple.
If the least common denominator is (1/24), color the space yellow.
If the least common denominator is (1/6), color the space green.

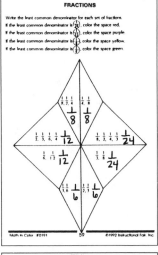

FRACTIONS

Write the least common denominator for each pair of fractions.
If the answer is (1/12), color the space yellow.
If the answer is (1/15), color the space blue.
If the answer is (1/18), color the space orange.
If the answer is (1/24), color the space purple.

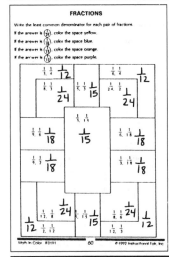

FRACTIONS

Find each sum and reduce to lowest terms if necessary.
If the sum is (1/2), color the space blue.
If the sum is (2/3), color the space green.
If the sum is (3/4), color the space red.

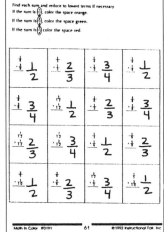

FRACTIONS

Change the fractions in each problem to common terms and add or subtract.
If the answer is (1/12), color the space purple.
If the answer is (11/12), color the space orange.
If the answer is (1/6), color the space yellow.
If the answer is (5/8), color the space green.
If the answer is (7/10), color the space red.

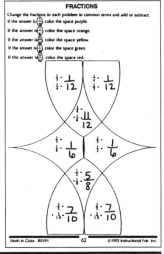

FRACTIONS

Find each difference and reduce if necessary.
If the difference is ($\frac{1}{4}$), color the space blue.
If the difference is ($\frac{1}{4}$), color the space red.
If the difference is ($\frac{1}{4}$), color the space green.
If the difference is ($\frac{1}{4}$), color the space orange.
If the difference is ($\frac{1}{4}$), color the space yellow.

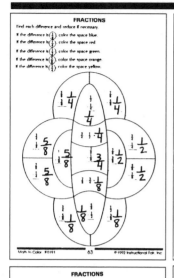

Math In Color #0191   63   ©1992 Instructional Fair, Inc.

FRACTIONS

Find each sum or difference and reduce answers when necessary.
If the answer is ($\frac{1}{12}$), color the space purple.
If the answer is ($\frac{1}{12}$), color the space green.
If the answer is ($\frac{1}{12}$), color the space yellow.
If the answer is ($\frac{11}{12}$), color the space red.

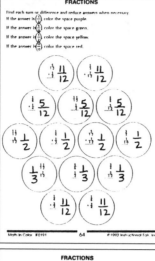

Math In Color #0191   64   ©1992 Instructional Fair, Inc.

FRACTIONS

Each improper fraction has an equivalent mixed number.
Write the numeral which correctly completes each mixed number.
If the numeral is (1), color the space orange.
If the numeral is (2), color the space green.
If the numeral is (3), color the space blue.
If the numeral is (4), color the space yellow.

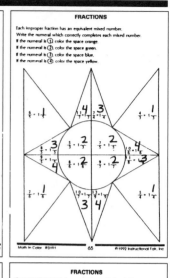

Math In Color #0191   65   ©1992 Instructional Fair, Inc.

FRACTIONS

Find each sum and change improper fractions to mixed numbers.
If the sum is $1\frac{5}{10}$, color the space yellow.
If the sum is ($1\frac{1}{5}$), color the space green.
If the sum is $1\frac{3}{10}$, color the space orange.
If the sum is $1\frac{7}{10}$, color the space red.

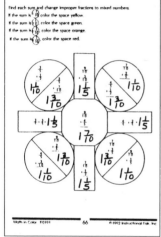

Math In Color #0191   66   ©1992 Instructional Fair, Inc.

FRACTIONS

Each mixed number has an equivalent improper fraction.
If the numeral is (7), color the space yellow.
If the numeral is (9), color the space orange.
If the numeral is (11), color the space red.

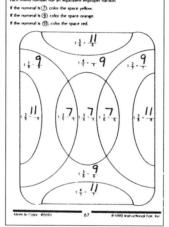

Math In Color #0191   67   ©1992 Instructional Fair, Inc.

FRACTIONS

Change mixed numbers to improper fractions and find each difference.
Reduce answers to lowest terms when necessary.
If the difference is ($\frac{1}{3}$), color the space green.
If the difference is ($\frac{1}{2}$), color the space orange.
If the difference is ($\frac{5}{6}$), color the space red.
If the difference is ($\frac{2}{3}$), color the space blue.

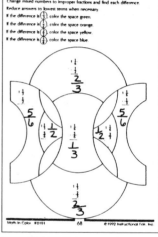

Math In Color #0191   68   ©1992 Instructional Fair, Inc.

FRACTIONS

Find each sum or difference and reduce answers to lowest terms when necessary.
If the answer is ($\frac{1}{2}$), color the space green.
If the answer is ($\frac{3}{8}$), color the space yellow.
If the answer is ($\frac{5}{8}$), color the space orange.
If the answer is ($\frac{1}{8}$), color the space blue.
If the answer is ($\frac{3}{4}$), color the space red.

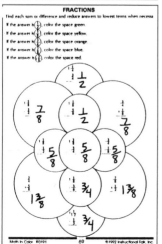

Math In Color #0191   69   ©1992 Instructional Fair, Inc.

FRACTIONS

Change each mixed number to a whole number and an improper fraction which is less than 2.
If the improper fraction is ($\frac{3}{2}$), color the space yellow.
If the improper fraction is ($\frac{5}{3}$) or ($\frac{5}{4}$), color the space red.
If the improper fraction is ($\frac{7}{5}$) or ($\frac{7}{4}$), color the space blue.
If the improper fraction is ($\frac{4}{3}$) or ($\frac{6}{5}$), color the space purple.

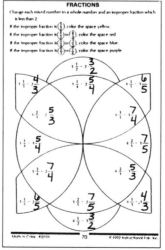

Math In Color #0191   70   ©1992 Instructional Fair, Inc.

FRACTIONS

Find each difference and reduce if necessary.
If the difference is ($\frac{1}{2}$), color the space yellow.
If the difference is ($\frac{5}{6}$), color the space green.
If the difference is ($\frac{2}{3}$), color the space blue.

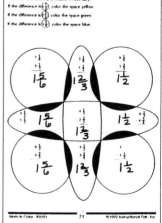

Math In Color #0191   71   ©1992 Instructional Fair, Inc.

DECIMALS

Find each product.
If the product is $.36$, 1.15, 2.56, or 3.44, color the space red.
If the product is 1.18, or 1.68, color the space brown.
If the product is 4.56, 6.30, 8.64, or 26.95, color the space yellow.
If the product is 5.46, 14.62, 15.12, or 19.04, color the space orange.

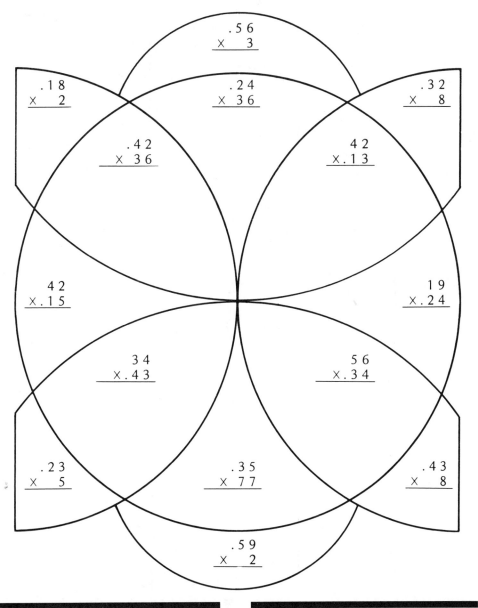

DECIMALS

Find each product.

If the product is (.12), (2.35), or (3.24), color the space red.

If the product is (.15), (.36), or (5.10), color the space blue.

If the product is (.18) or (15.96), color the space green.

If the product is (.24) or (30.24), color the space orange.

If the product is (1.12), (1.28), (1.35), (9.90), (18.36), or (22.32), color the space
   yellow.

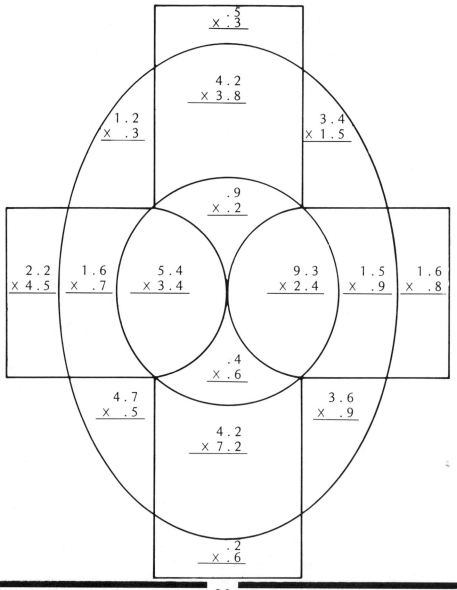

DECIMALS

Find each product.
If the product is $\widehat{.045}$, $\widehat{.224}$, or $\widehat{2.185}$, color the space orange.
If the product is $\widehat{.060}$, $\widehat{.105}$, $\widehat{1.136}$, or $\widehat{1.998}$, color the space red.
If the product is $\widehat{.094}$, $\widehat{1.848}$, or $\widehat{2.821}$, color the space yellow.

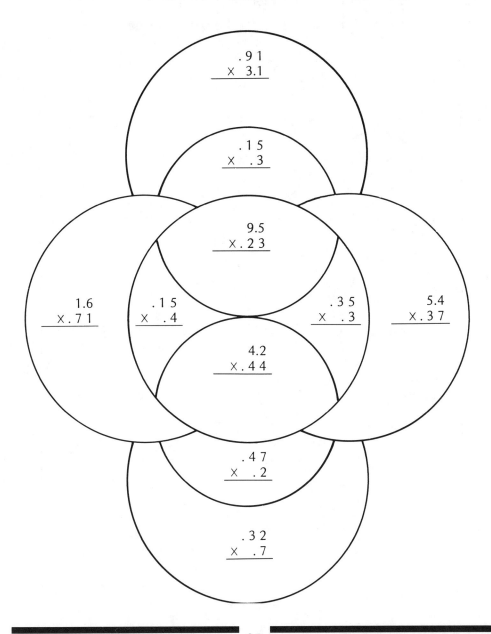

DECIMALS

Find each product.
If the product is .0646 or .4521, color the space purple.
If the product is .1980, .2491, .2520, or .3640, color the space yellow.
If the product is .3105 or 1.2524, color the space red.
If the product is 1.3680 or 1.5300, color the space orange.

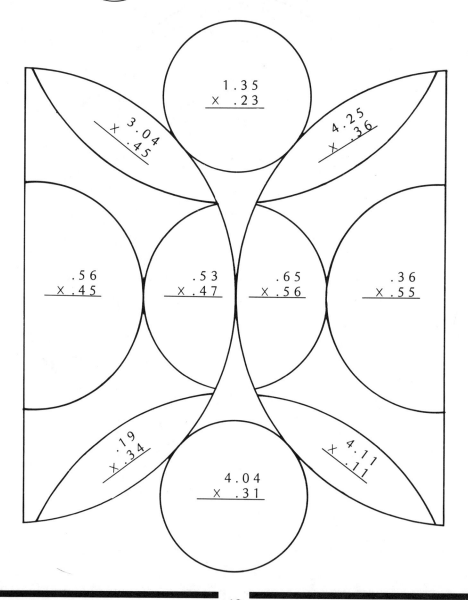

DECIMALS

Find each product.
If the product is (.15), (.28), (3.6), or (.91), color the space green.
If the product is (.225), (3.70), (7.98), or (219.6), color the space purple.
If the product is (.36), (2.646), (6.256), (30.0), or (277.5), color the space orange.

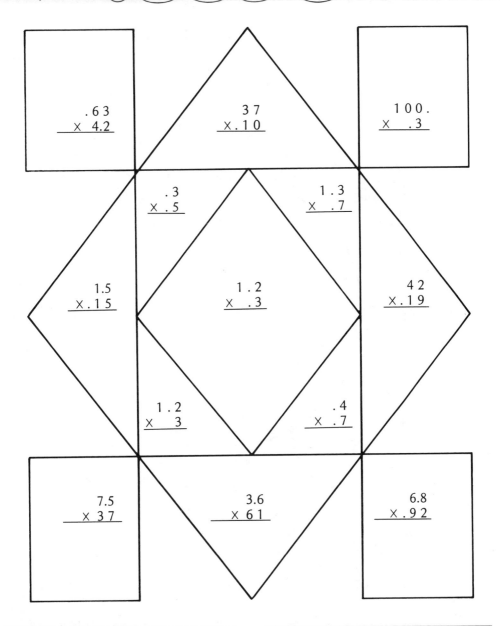

$$
\begin{array}{r} .63 \\ \times \ 4.2 \\ \hline \end{array}
$$

$$
\begin{array}{r} 37 \\ \times .10 \\ \hline \end{array}
$$

$$
\begin{array}{r} 100. \\ \times \quad .3 \\ \hline \end{array}
$$

$$
\begin{array}{r} .3 \\ \times .5 \\ \hline \end{array}
$$

$$
\begin{array}{r} 1.3 \\ \times \ .7 \\ \hline \end{array}
$$

$$
\begin{array}{r} 1.5 \\ \times .15 \\ \hline \end{array}
$$

$$
\begin{array}{r} 1.2 \\ \times \ .3 \\ \hline \end{array}
$$

$$
\begin{array}{r} 42 \\ \times .19 \\ \hline \end{array}
$$

$$
\begin{array}{r} 1.2 \\ \times \quad 3 \\ \hline \end{array}
$$

$$
\begin{array}{r} .4 \\ \times .7 \\ \hline \end{array}
$$

$$
\begin{array}{r} 7.5 \\ \times \ 37 \\ \hline \end{array}
$$

$$
\begin{array}{r} 3.6 \\ \times \ 61 \\ \hline \end{array}
$$

$$
\begin{array}{r} 6.8 \\ \times .92 \\ \hline \end{array}
$$

DECIMALS

Find each quotient.
If the quotient is ⑫, color the space red.
If the quotient is ⑬, color the space yellow.
If the quotient is ⑰, color the space purple.

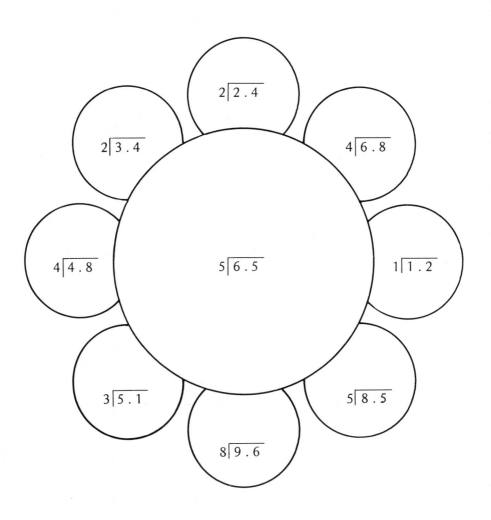

DECIMALS

Find each quotient.
If the quotient is (8.5), color the space green.
If the quotient is (9.5), color the space red.
If the quotient is (16.5), color the space purple.
If the quotient is (22.5), color the space yellow.

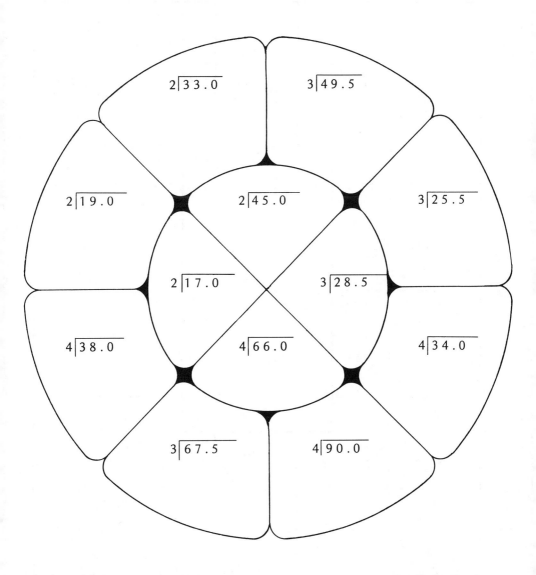

DECIMALS

Find each quotient.
If the quotient is (18.3), color the space green.
If the quotient is (19.1), color the space yellow.
If the quotient is (19.5), color the space blue.

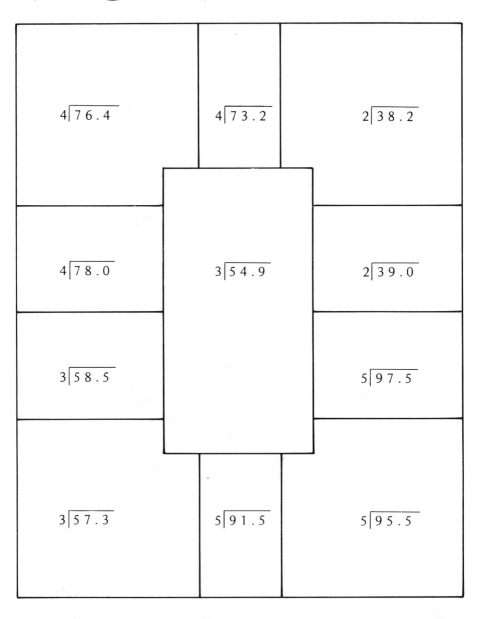

DECIMALS

Find each quotient.
If the quotient is ⟨.48⟩, color the space green.
If the quotient is ⟨54⟩, color the space yellow.
If the quotient is ⟨48.⟩, color the space blue.

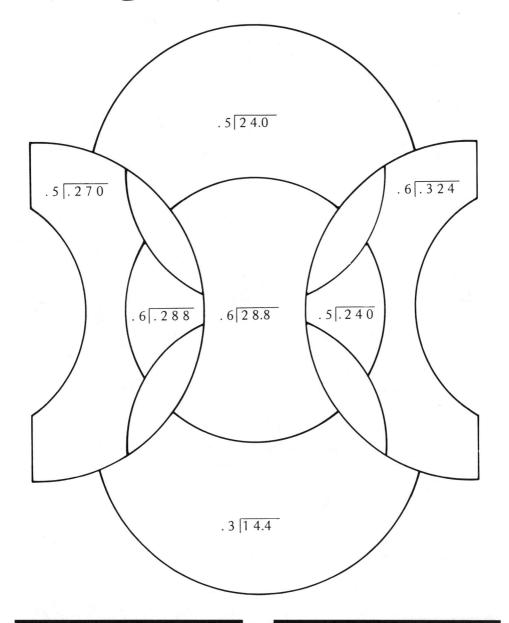

FRACTIONS

Find each sum.

If the sum is $\frac{7}{12}$, color the space red.

If the sum is $\frac{8}{12}$, color the space blue.

If the sum is $\frac{9}{12}$, color the space yellow.

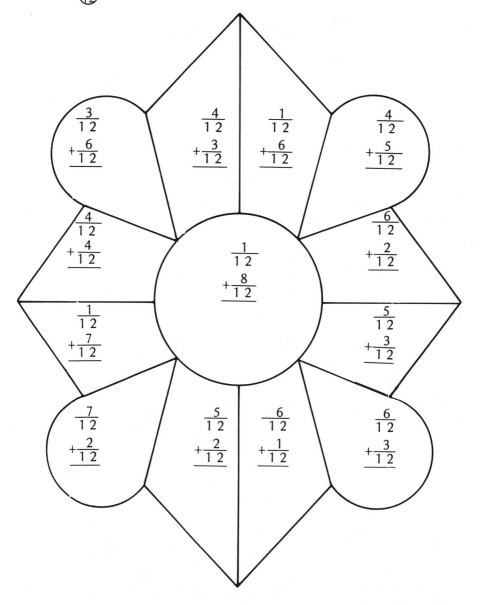

FRACTIONS

Find each sum.

If the sum is $\left(\frac{5}{12}\right)$, color the space blue.

If the sum is $\left(\frac{7}{12}\right)$, color the space yellow.

If the sum is $\left(\frac{9}{12}\right)$, color the space purple.

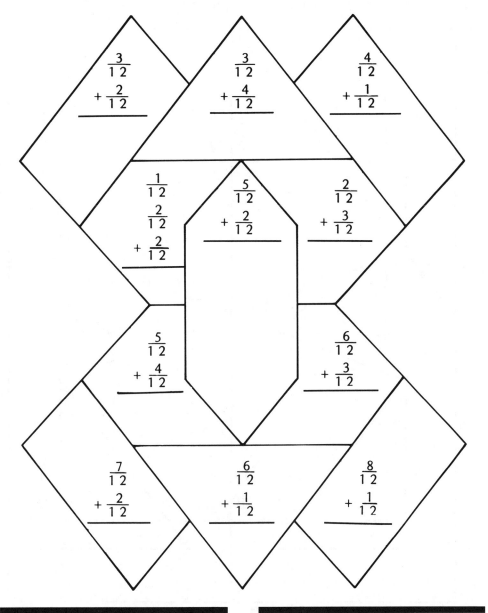

FRACTIONS

Find each difference.

If the difference is $\left(\frac{1}{8}\right)$, color the space yellow.

If the difference is $\left(\frac{2}{8}\right)$, color the space blue.

If the difference is $\left(\frac{3}{8}\right)$, color the space orange.

If the difference is $\left(\frac{4}{8}\right)$, color the space purple.

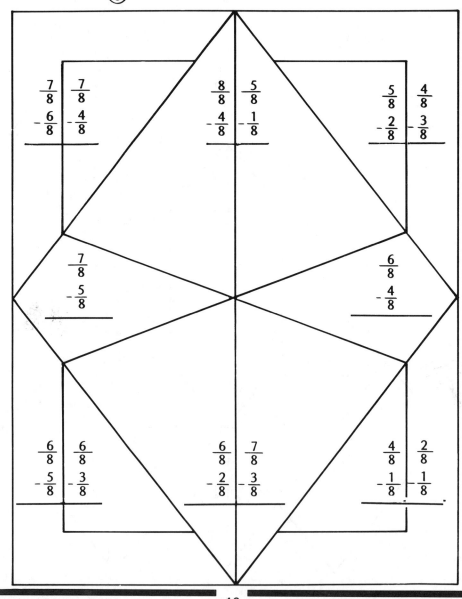

48

FRACTIONS

Find each difference.

If the difference is $\left(\frac{1}{12}\right)$, color the space yellow.

If the difference is $\left(\frac{2}{12}\right)$, color the space blue.

If the difference is $\left(\frac{5}{12}\right)$, color the space orange.

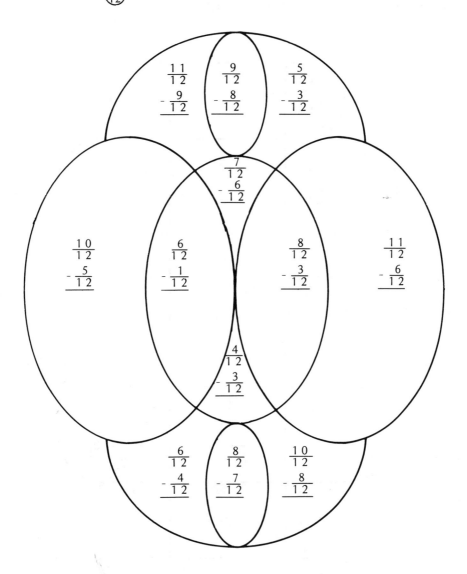

FRACTIONS

Find each sum or difference.

If the answer is $\frac{6}{12}$, color the space green.

If the answer is $\frac{7}{12}$, color the space blue.

If the answer is $\frac{8}{12}$, color the space yellow.

If the answer is $\frac{9}{12}$, color the space purple.

$\frac{5}{12}$ $+\frac{1}{12}$	$\frac{4}{12}$ $+\frac{4}{12}$	$\frac{11}{12}$ $-\frac{5}{12}$
$\frac{3}{12}$ $+\frac{3}{12}$	$\frac{9}{12}$ $-\frac{1}{12}$	$\frac{7}{12}$ $-\frac{1}{12}$
$\frac{5}{12}$ $+\frac{2}{12}$	$\frac{9}{12}$ $-\frac{2}{12}$	$\frac{11}{12}$ $-\frac{4}{12}$
$\frac{5}{12}$ $+\frac{4}{12}$	$\frac{10}{12}$ $-\frac{2}{12}$	$\frac{11}{12}$ $-\frac{2}{12}$
$\frac{8}{12}$ $+\frac{1}{12}$	$\frac{5}{12}$ $+\frac{3}{12}$	$\frac{10}{12}$ $-\frac{1}{12}$

FRACTIONS

If the pair of fractions is equivalent, color the space green.
If the pair of fractions is not equivalent, color the space red.

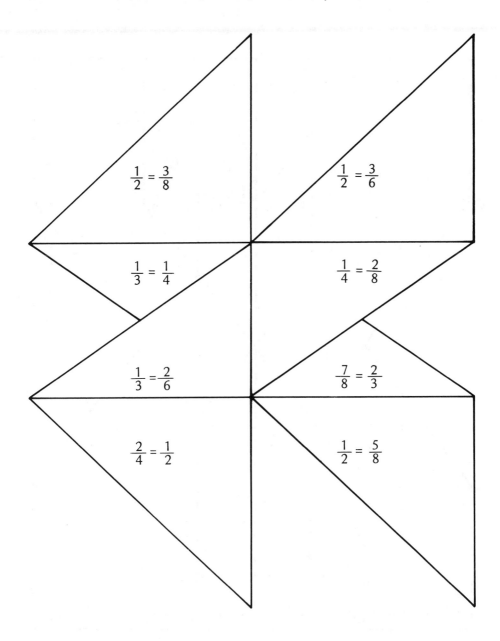

$\frac{1}{2} = \frac{3}{8}$

$\frac{1}{2} = \frac{3}{6}$

$\frac{1}{3} = \frac{1}{4}$

$\frac{1}{4} = \frac{2}{8}$

$\frac{1}{3} = \frac{2}{6}$

$\frac{7}{8} = \frac{2}{3}$

$\frac{2}{4} = \frac{1}{2}$

$\frac{1}{2} = \frac{5}{8}$

FRACTIONS

If the pair of fractions is equivalent, color the space yellow.
If the pair of fractions is not equivalent, color the space green.

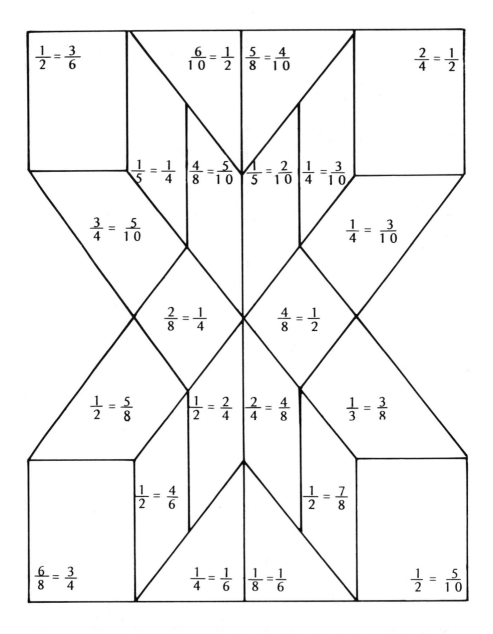

$\frac{1}{2} = \frac{3}{6}$

$\frac{6}{10} = \frac{1}{2}$ $\frac{5}{8} = \frac{4}{10}$

$\frac{2}{4} = \frac{1}{2}$

$\frac{1}{5} = \frac{1}{4}$ $\frac{4}{8} = \frac{5}{10}$ $\frac{1}{5} = \frac{2}{10}$ $\frac{1}{4} = \frac{3}{10}$

$\frac{3}{4} = \frac{5}{10}$

$\frac{1}{4} = \frac{3}{10}$

$\frac{2}{8} = \frac{1}{4}$

$\frac{4}{8} = \frac{1}{2}$

$\frac{1}{2} = \frac{5}{8}$ $\frac{1}{2} = \frac{2}{4}$ $\frac{2}{4} = \frac{4}{8}$ $\frac{1}{3} = \frac{3}{8}$

$\frac{1}{2} = \frac{4}{6}$ $\frac{1}{2} = \frac{7}{8}$

$\frac{6}{8} = \frac{3}{4}$ $\frac{1}{4} = \frac{1}{6}$ $\frac{1}{8} = \frac{1}{6}$ $\frac{1}{2} = \frac{5}{10}$

FRACTIONS

Write a numeral to complete each pair of equivalent fractions.

If the answer is ②, color the space blue.

If the answer is ③, color the space yellow.

If the answer is ④, color the space green.

If the answer is ⑧, color the space purple.

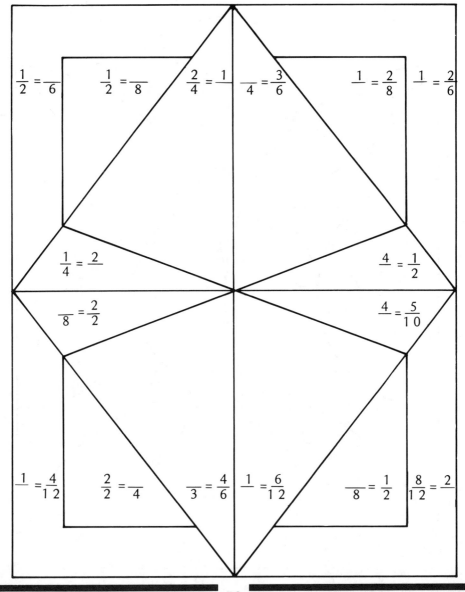

$$\frac{1}{2} = \frac{}{6}$$ $$\frac{1}{2} = \frac{}{8}$$ $$\frac{2}{4} = \frac{1}{}$$ $$\frac{}{4} = \frac{3}{6}$$ $$\frac{1}{} = \frac{2}{8}$$ $$\frac{1}{} = \frac{2}{6}$$

$$\frac{1}{4} = \frac{2}{}$$ $$\frac{4}{} = \frac{1}{2}$$

$$\frac{}{8} = \frac{2}{2}$$ $$\frac{4}{} = \frac{5}{10}$$

$$\frac{1}{} = \frac{4}{12}$$ $$\frac{2}{2} = \frac{4}{}$$ $$\frac{}{3} = \frac{4}{6}$$ $$\frac{1}{} = \frac{6}{12}$$ $$\frac{}{8} = \frac{1}{2}$$ $$\frac{8}{12} = \frac{2}{}$$

FRACTIONS

Write a numeral to complete each pair of equivalent fractions.
If the answer is ②, color the space green.
If the answer is ④, color the space blue.
If the answer is ⑤, color the space orange.
If the answer is ⑩, color the space purple.

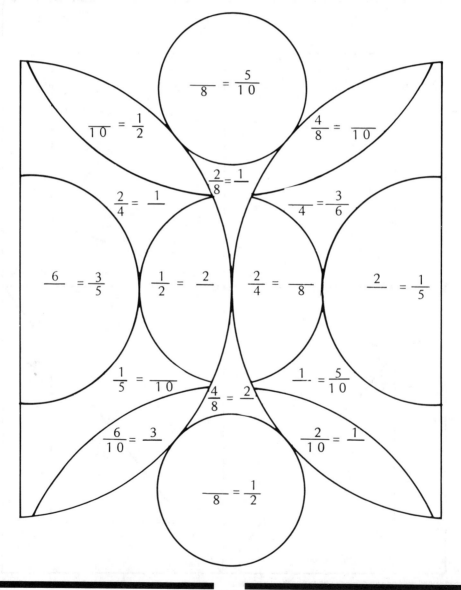

FRACTIONS

Reduce each fraction to lowest terms.

If the answer is $\frac{1}{4}$, color the space red.

If the answer is $\frac{1}{3}$, color the space yellow.

If the answer is $\frac{1}{2}$, color the space blue.

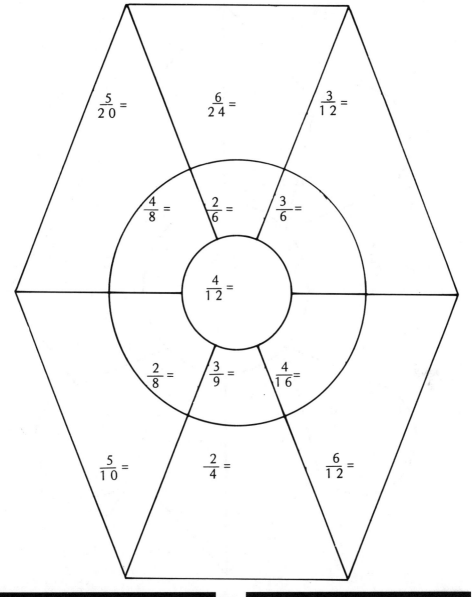

FRACTIONS

Reduce each fraction to lowest terms.

If the answer is $\frac{1}{4}$, color the space blue.

If the answer is $\frac{1}{3}$, color the space orange.

If the answer is $\frac{1}{2}$, color the space green.

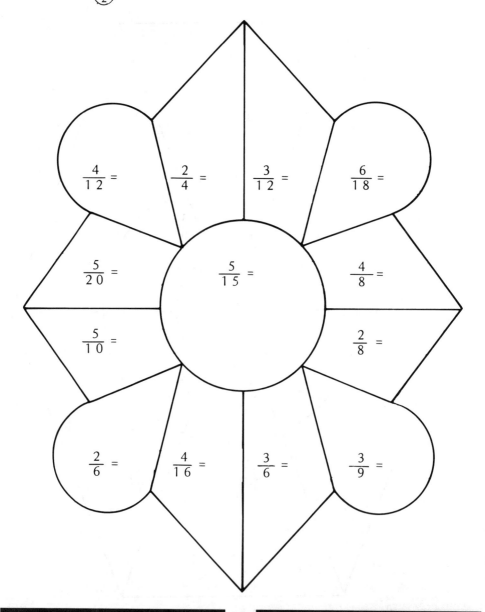

FRACTIONS

Reduce each fraction to lowest terms.

If the answer is $\left(\frac{1}{5}\right)$, color the space purple.

If the answer is $\left(\frac{1}{2}\right)$, color the space orange.

If the answer is $\left(\frac{2}{3}\right)$, color the space yellow.

If the answer is $\left(\frac{3}{4}\right)$, color the space red.

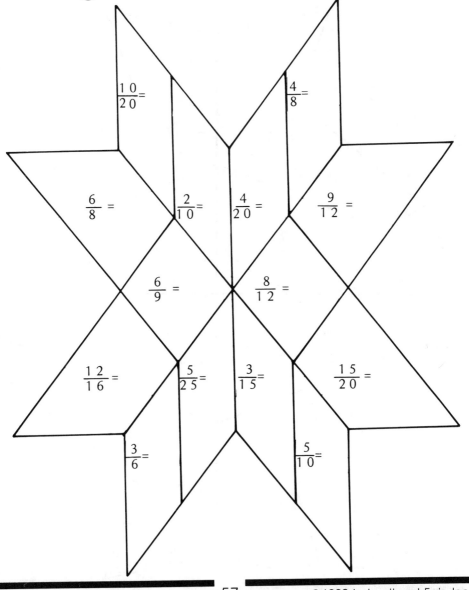

Math in Color   IF0191   ©1992 Instructional Fair, Inc.

FRACTIONS

Write the least common denominator for each set of fractions.

If the least common denominator is $\left(\frac{1}{12}\right)$, color the space yellow.

If the least common denominator is $\left(\frac{1}{8}\right)$, color the space green.

If the least common denominator is $\left(\frac{1}{6}\right)$, color the space purple.

If the least common denominator is $\left(\frac{1}{4}\right)$, color the space red.

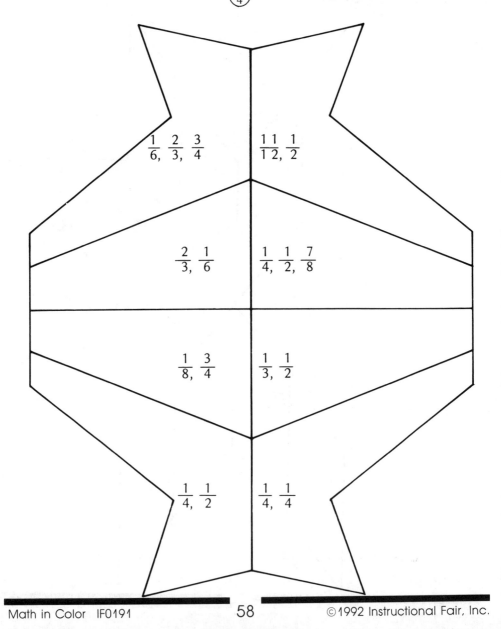

FRACTIONS

Write the least common denominator for each set of fractions.
If the least common denominator is $\frac{1}{24}$, color the space red.
If the least common denominator is $\frac{1}{12}$, color the space purple.
If the least common denominator is $\frac{1}{8}$, color the space yellow.
If the least common denominator is $\frac{1}{6}$, color the space green.

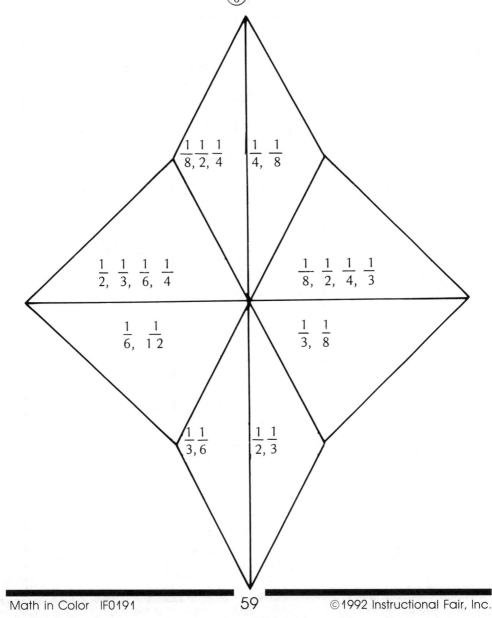

FRACTIONS

Write the least common denominator for each pair of fractions.

If the answer is $\frac{1}{24}$, color the space yellow.

If the answer is $\frac{1}{18}$, color the space blue.

If the answer is $\frac{1}{15}$, color the space orange.

If the answer is $\frac{1}{12}$, color the space purple.

$\frac{1}{3}, \frac{1}{4}$

$\frac{1}{6}, \frac{1}{4}$

$\frac{1}{8}, \frac{1}{3}$

$\frac{1}{5}, \frac{1}{3}$

$\frac{1}{2\,4}, \frac{1}{2}$

$\frac{1}{3}, \frac{1}{1\,5}$

$\frac{1}{9}, \frac{1}{6}$

$\frac{1}{6}, \frac{1}{1\,8}$

$\frac{1}{9}, \frac{1}{2}$

$\frac{1}{3}, \frac{1}{1\,8}$

$\frac{1}{1\,2}, \frac{1}{8}$

$\frac{1}{5}, \frac{1}{1\,5}$

$\frac{1}{8}, \frac{1}{6}$

$\frac{1}{2}, \frac{1}{1\,2}$

$\frac{1}{1\,2}, \frac{1}{3}$

FRACTIONS

Find each sum and reduce to lowest terms if necessary.

If the sum is $\frac{1}{2}$, color the space orange.

If the sum is $\frac{2}{3}$, color the space green.

If the sum is $\frac{3}{4}$ color the space red.

$\frac{1}{8}$ $+\frac{3}{8}$	$\frac{1}{3}$ $+\frac{1}{3}$	$\frac{1}{4}$ $+\frac{1}{2}$	$\frac{1}{4}$ $+\frac{1}{4}$
$\frac{3}{8}$ $+\frac{3}{8}$	$\frac{5}{12}$ $+\frac{1}{12}$	$\frac{1}{6}$ $+\frac{1}{2}$	$\frac{5}{8}$ $+\frac{1}{8}$
$\frac{7}{12}$ $+\frac{1}{12}$	$\frac{7}{12}$ $+\frac{2}{12}$	$\frac{1}{3}$ $+\frac{1}{6}$	$\frac{1}{9}$ $+\frac{5}{9}$
$\frac{2}{5}$ $+\frac{1}{10}$	$\frac{2}{9}$ $+\frac{4}{9}$	$\frac{5}{12}$ $+\frac{1}{3}$	$\frac{1}{5}$ $+\frac{3}{10}$

FRACTIONS

Change the fractions in each problem to common terms and add or subtract.

If the answer is $\left(\frac{1}{12}\right)$, color the space purple.

If the answer is $\left(\frac{1}{6}\right)$, color the space orange.

If the answer is $\left(\frac{5}{8}\right)$, color the space yellow.

If the answer is $\left(\frac{7}{10}\right)$, color the space green.

If the answer is $\left(\frac{11}{12}\right)$, color the space red.

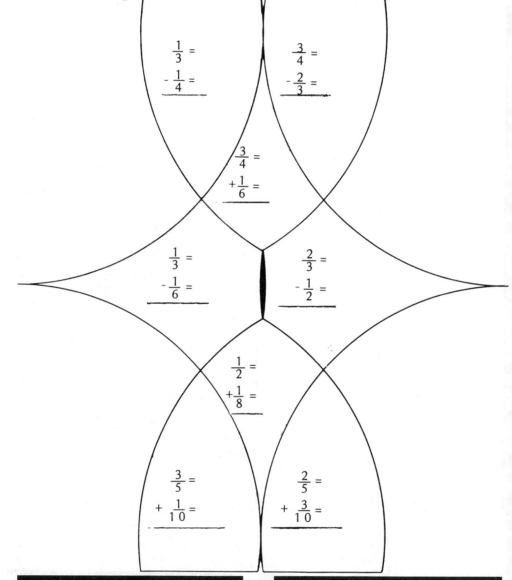

$$\frac{1}{3} =$$
$$-\frac{1}{4} =$$
___

$$\frac{3}{4} =$$
$$-\frac{2}{3} =$$
___

$$\frac{3}{4} =$$
$$+\frac{1}{6} =$$
___

$$\frac{1}{3} =$$
$$-\frac{1}{6} =$$
___

$$\frac{2}{3} =$$
$$-\frac{1}{2} =$$
___

$$\frac{1}{2} =$$
$$+\frac{1}{8} =$$
___

$$\frac{3}{5} =$$
$$+\frac{1}{10} =$$
___

$$\frac{2}{5} =$$
$$+\frac{3}{10} =$$
___

FRACTIONS

Find each difference and reduce if necessary.

If the difference is $\left(\frac{1}{8}\right)$, color the space blue.

If the difference is $\left(\frac{1}{4}\right)$, color the space red.

If the difference is $\left(\frac{1}{2}\right)$, color the space green.

If the difference is $\left(\frac{5}{8}\right)$, color the space orange.

If the difference is $\left(\frac{3}{4}\right)$, color the space yellow.

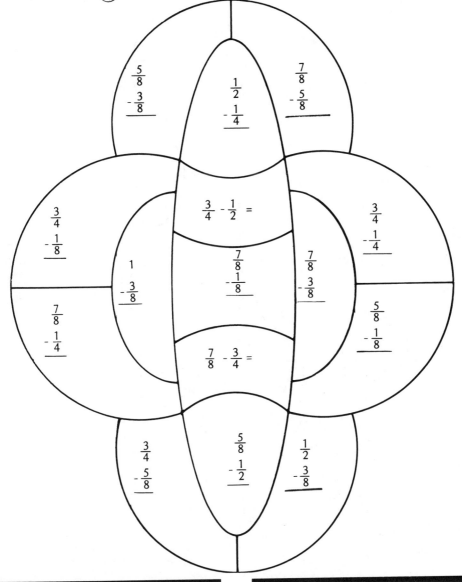

FRACTIONS

Find each sum or difference and reduce answers when necessary.

If the answer is $\frac{1}{3}$, color the space purple.

If the answer is $\frac{5}{12}$, color the space green.

If the answer is $\frac{1}{2}$, color the space yellow.

If the answer is $\frac{11}{12}$, color the space red.

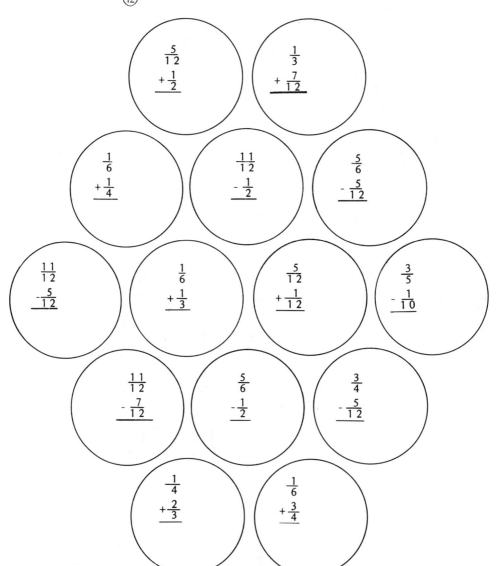

FRACTIONS

Each improper fraction has an equivalent mixed number.
Write the numeral which correctly completes each mixed number.
If the numeral is ① color the space orange.
If the numeral is ② color the space green.
If the numeral is ③ color the space blue.
If the numeral is ④ color the space yellow.

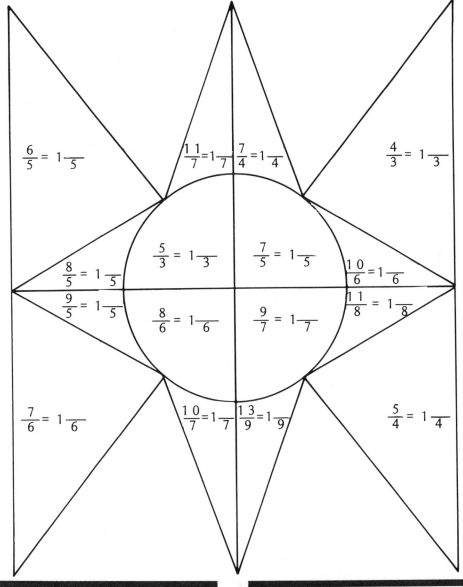

FRACTIONS

Find each sum and change improper fractions to mixed numbers.
If the sum is $1\frac{1}{10}$, color the space yellow.
If the sum is $1\frac{1}{5}$, color the space green.
If the sum is $1\frac{3}{10}$, color the space orange.
If the sum is $1\frac{7}{10}$, color the space red.

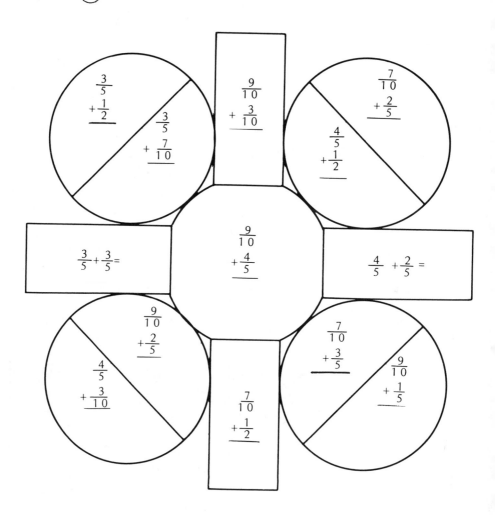

FRACTIONS

Each mixed number has an equivalent improper fraction.

If the numeral is ⑦, color the space yellow.

If the numeral is ⑨, color the space orange.

If the numeral is ⑪, color the space red.

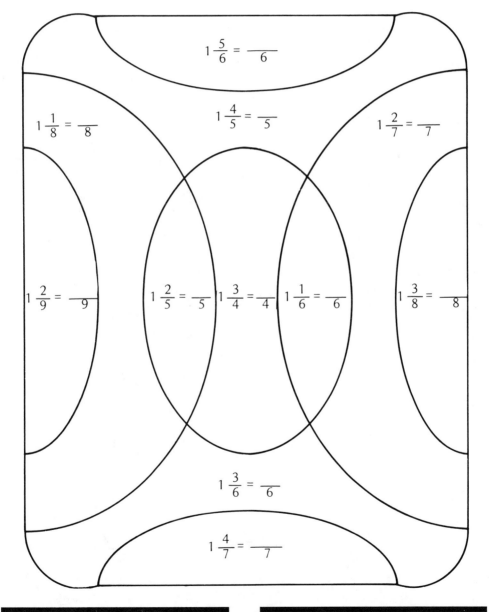

$1\frac{5}{6} = \frac{}{6}$

$1\frac{1}{8} = \frac{}{8}$

$1\frac{4}{5} = \frac{}{5}$

$1\frac{2}{7} = \frac{}{7}$

$1\frac{2}{9} = \frac{}{9}$

$1\frac{2}{5} = \frac{}{5}$

$1\frac{3}{4} = \frac{}{4}$

$1\frac{1}{6} = \frac{}{6}$

$1\frac{3}{8} = \frac{}{8}$

$1\frac{3}{6} = \frac{}{6}$

$1\frac{4}{7} = \frac{}{7}$

FRACTIONS

Change mixed numbers to improper fractions and find each difference.

Reduce answers to lowest terms when necessary.

If the difference is $\left(\frac{1}{3}\right)$, color the space green.

If the difference is $\left(\frac{1}{2}\right)$, color the space orange.

If the difference is $\left(\frac{2}{3}\right)$, color the space yellow.

If the difference is $\left(\frac{5}{6}\right)$, color the space blue.

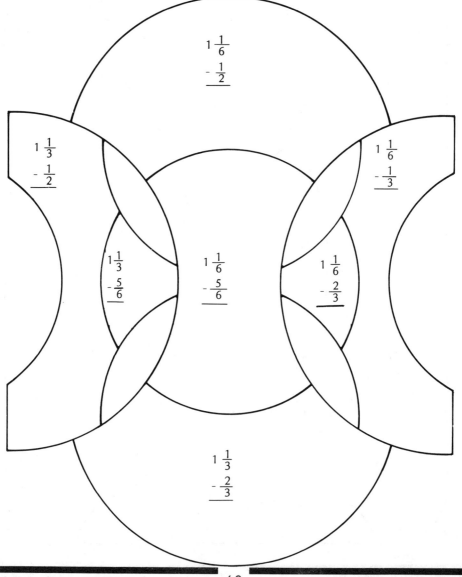

FRACTIONS

Find each sum or difference and reduce answers to lowest terms when necessary.

If the answer is $\left(\frac{1}{2}\right)$, color the space green.

If the answer is $\left(\frac{5}{8}\right)$, color the space yellow.

If the answer is $\left(\frac{3}{4}\right)$, color the space orange.

If the answer is $\left(\frac{7}{8}\right)$, color the space blue.

If the answer is $\left(1\frac{3}{8}\right)$, color the space red.

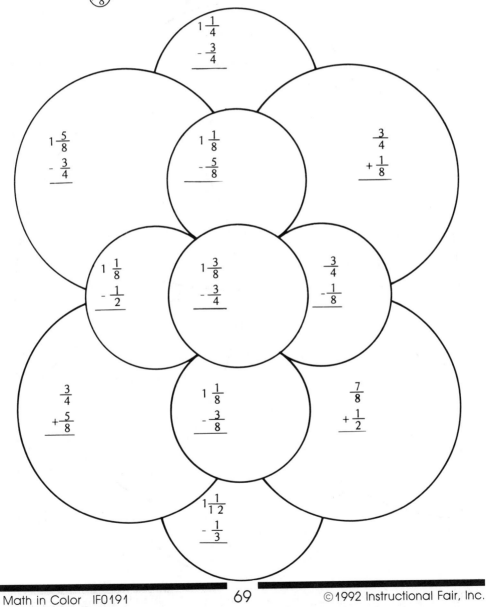

FRACTIONS

Change each mixed number to a whole number and an improper fraction which
is less than 2.

If the improper fraction is $\left(\frac{3}{2}\right)$, color the space yellow.

If the improper fraction is $\left(\frac{4}{3}\right)$ or $\left(\frac{6}{5}\right)$, color the space red.

If the improper fraction is $\left(\frac{5}{4}\right)$ or $\left(\frac{7}{5}\right)$, color the space blue.

If the improper fraction is $\left(\frac{5}{3}\right)$ or $\left(\frac{7}{4}\right)$, color the space purple.

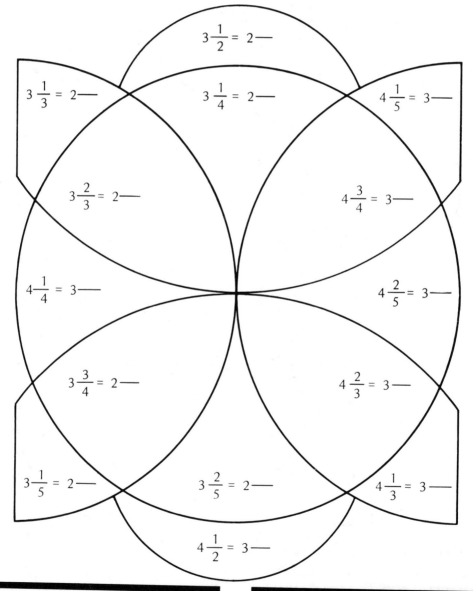

FRACTIONS

Find each difference and reduce if necessary.

If the difference is $\left(1\frac{1}{2}\right)$, color the space yellow.

If the difference is $\left(1\frac{2}{3}\right)$, color the space green.

If the difference is $\left(1\frac{5}{6}\right)$, color the space blue.

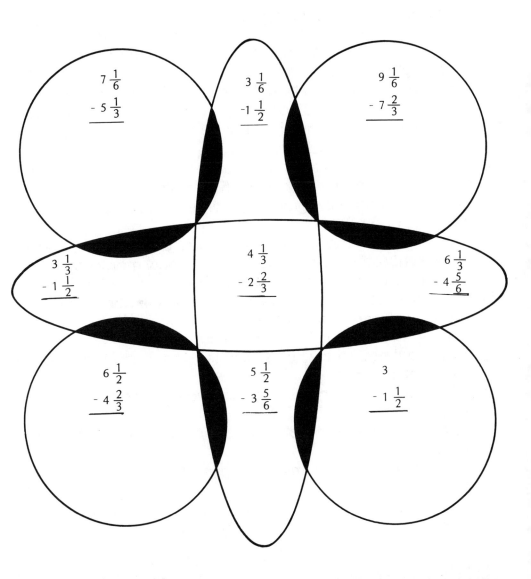

$7\frac{1}{6}$
$-5\frac{1}{3}$

$3\frac{1}{6}$
$-1\frac{1}{2}$

$9\frac{1}{6}$
$-7\frac{2}{3}$

$3\frac{1}{3}$
$-1\frac{1}{2}$

$4\frac{1}{3}$
$-2\frac{2}{3}$

$6\frac{1}{3}$
$-4\frac{5}{6}$

$6\frac{1}{2}$
$-4\frac{2}{3}$

$5\frac{1}{2}$
$-3\frac{5}{6}$

3
$-1\frac{1}{2}$

Help-at-Home Activities

Below are some activities to do with your child at home.

1. Play popcorn math. Example: Have $5\frac{1}{2}$ cups, you ate $2\frac{1}{4}$ cups. How many cups are left over?
2. Measure a room together.
3. Give your child a ruler to measure his/her leg, foot, hand, arm, etc.
4. Use candy to make math problems.
5. Take a picture of your child. Write height and weight on back. Repeat once a month. Write problems to compare the heights and weights.
6. Read a newspaper article that deals with numbers and graphs. Make up problems with the numbers and graphs.
7. Look at a recipe. Have him/her double and triple the recipe. Make sure it contains fractions.
8. Do 4 math problems using something in your kitchen. Example: 50 beans divided by 5 beans equals?
9. With coins and bills, figure out 5 different ways to make $10, $25, $50 and $100.
10. Figure out how many hours, minutes and seconds he/she will be in school this week. Also figure out how many hours, minutes and seconds he/she will spend on homework.
11. Look at a grocery ad. Tell your child he/she can spend $50. Have him/her make up a list of things to buy. Remind the child to think about the 4 food groups.
12. Figure out how many hours, minutes and seconds he/she will be awake today.
13. Figure out how many days, hours and minutes there are until his/her birthday.
14. Write a math word problem whose answer is equal to today's date.
15. Compare prices of items at the grocery store. Which is the best buy, etc.